The Library of Lives volume 1, *The Falling Light*

© Z D Finn 2021

zdfinn.com

Illustrations: Anatole Beams

anatolebeams@abdm.co.uk

© Poetry: David Davidson

fromagreenhill.com

Poetry: Z D Finn

zdfinn.wordpress.com

ISBN 978-1-915292-14-8

Printed in the United Kingdom.

First edition, 2021. Second edition for print and online, 2022.

Published by Applied Meditation Ltd.

A new dawn

I've heard people say
that our future depends
on us changing our attitudes,
becoming more loving to one another
and that we will be made aware of this
through catastrophe and natural disaster.

But the changes we need
have already happened,
they are just waiting for us
to recognise them.

If Love is God
then it doesn't need
an earthquake, a pandemic
or crazy leaders to make itself known,
when it comes it will be as a
gentle dawning in our hearts,
all it needs from us
is that we trust it
when it does.

David Davidson 2020

Acknowledgements

Strangely, perhaps the writing of this book has made me feel grateful for all the aspects of my life, even the hardest and most painful ones, for that is where the experience and the learning has been the most heartfelt. Unfortunately, more in retrospect than at the time.

I am thankful for the support of my family; David Davidson who is a beautiful poet and channel in his own right and my two sons, daughter-in-law and granddaughter, a little family, much loved and source of eternal joy and gratitude.

Particular thanks to my nephew Anatole Beams who has provided images and designs for so many of my projects including this one and he does so with such grace and style.

Thank you to Michael whose encouragement led me to value and publish 'Lost & Found & Lost again', which opened the door to this volume and to those that have followed in its wake.

The alpha and omega of thanks goes to my friends, spiritual companions, colleagues, and Teachers who have walked beside me every step of the way and never given up on me even when I have given up on myself.

Contents

Introduction

Welcome to the inner world of Dorothy Marsden, a world that has expanded as her outer life has contracted. Where once Dorothy was busy with careers, friends and a young family, advancing age, unexpected retirement and a pandemic have conspired to create acres of empty time. Every day is suddenly like the Sundays of her childhood and so, along with so many others, she has had to relearn how to sit still.

At first, she sought distractions, but found very little sustenance in the numerous TV channels she would flick idly through. Cleaning out the detritus from her 30-year-old kitchen cabinets was more satisfying and led to the emptying of many more cupboards, but once that need was satiated, she started to question what all this space was for? On the face of it more emptiness was the last thing she needed, surely she needed activity and to feel useful once again?

Dorothy has always been a mutterer. Those who know her well are accustomed to overhearing the tail end of any number of imaginary encounters as they enter her company. It is physical too, should they catch her unawares they would often be met by a shocked expression as Dorothy oriented herself to their arrival and away from her inner musings. But now it is this inner dialogue that has centre stage, that has overcome her initial resistance and expanded itself away from the minutiae of life to the purpose of life, her life in particular, and all life in general.

There is no telling where her tendency towards inner dialogue came from, or even if it is that unusual, but her early childhood was one that encouraged a withdrawal from life, not an embracing of it. She comes from a fractured background, one which continued to splinter throughout her childhood, meaning her contact with family was minimal and long-term friendships impossible until her teenage years.

So, self-reliance was essential, and Dorothy can recall in detail the time and place when she realised she was alone. Now many may consider such a realisation in a twelve-year-old child unhelpful and in many ways it was, it led to a complicated adolescence and an abrupt departure from home. But maybe, just maybe, it is also the source of Dorothy's abiding sense that the world is impermanent, that there is something greater and more important than the structures and mores of society. Dorothy always felt she was cocooned by some invisible magnetic force that held her in its sway and kept her safe, and perhaps she was right.

She certainly found the strength to make a new life in a new city at sixteen and to pursue education and navigate the world of work courageously, given her background, if not bordering on the foolhardy. She found love and has nurtured and been nurtured in a new family where the bonds are strong and the respect is deep.

This belief, which accompanied her sense of loss, has been a driving force and a source of great comfort and challenge over the last thirty years. It has led her to channels and spiritual Teachers to whom she owes a great deal. They have opened her eyes and her heart in so many ways that now when she sits quietly, and the world around her is silent too, that inner dialogue is rich with imagery and interwoven with peace.

She sits, her hair white now, in the same corner of the living room that she always inhabits first thing. A cup of tea by her side and the light of her iPad framing her face. Around her magnificent crystals sit on light boxes, fresh lilies fill the grate, silence fills the street and her partner is already out walking in the early morning camera in hand ready to illustrate his latest poem. Then she raises her hands sounds an Aum and says a prayer ... and then writes, without censorship, what comes.

Why? She does not know, but at times, like today, the words wake her up demanding that they be recorded for they have something they wish to bring to this earth. An earth that at this time is rife with disease and fear, where people are suffering and despairing as the only way of life they have known seems to be slipping away and they see no other means of survival. It is almost as if that sense of impermanence, so familiar to Dorothy, has become universal and that may feel like an awakening to some, but as a terrifying end to many.

As she sits, she allows the tides of loss and helplessness to move through her before picking up her screen and typing, silently, on the smooth glass delicately balancing on her lap. Should you look closely, her lips are moving to the words that are actively seeking the light of the screen from within the darkness of the night and the darkness that surrounds the earth at this time. Words fall like ribbons of gold onto the page, like water onto parched earth, as Dorothy holds out her net so that others may share her bounty.

Stepping out of time

Dorothy: 'Aum ... I believe in the Light.'

Librarian: 'Then follow it, don't direct it, follow. What do you see?'

Dorothy: 'A wall of books stretching into infinity, leather-bound, gold glinting of them. Each one as tall as a person, standing one upon the other reaching far above me, too far to sense any ceiling and too far into the distance to sense any end.

'Now as my eyes focus I sense movement, perhaps they are not books at all but Beings of Light glinting in some hidden light, as still as statutes and yet, there is movement. I am looking at what could be described as a wall of Archangels, although my experience of Archangels is rather limited, and the imagery is subtle and moving but beautiful. A wall of Light and colour that distils into separate images and then merges again like the sea moving over the sand in the moonlight.'

Librarian: 'All that is left to the human mind it to interpret.'

Dorothy: 'At first, I thought they were whispering to each other, but that's not right. Now, I sense motes of Light flashing into and around these forms making it appear as if they are moving, but they are not, they're as still as time itself. For everything now feels timeless, as if I have stepped through a portal and the sea is rushing though me too.'

Librarian: 'What are you feeling?'

Dorothy: 'I'm feeling absolutely still, rooted to the spot and strangely ancient, timeless, empty of life, but full at the same time.'

Librarian: 'Close your eyes and follow the motes.'

Dorothy: 'At first I see downtown LA at night, the highways filled with car lights moving in a man made sequence of roads and patterns. Then the night sky filled with tiny stars pulsating in a rhythm that appear random until you uncover the patterns. I catch one in the palm of my hand and it's pulsating with life. Is it a life?'

Librarian: 'Yes, they are returning souls bringing their bounty of life back home.'

Dorothy: 'Wait, some are moving in another direction, are they returning to earth?'

Librarian: 'Some yes, they have visited for a while and now need to return, some are being born.'

Dorothy: 'Visited, who have they visited?'

Librarian: 'Their Higher Self, their source of knowledge and purpose.'

Dorothy: 'Do all souls visit?'

Librarian: 'Do you mean those in life?'

Dorothy: 'Yes, I suppose I do.'

Librarian: 'Most do, look again at the motes and what do you see, are they all the same?'

Dorothy: 'They are all the same size, but the colours are so different. Some are vibrant, jewel like, some are dull almost a grey and they move at a different speed too.

'Wait, some are not individual, they are being guided by winged beings that flash gold and silver and hold their charges like a mother holds her newborn baby. Where do they lay them?'

Librarian: 'They aren't laid anywhere as they have no form, they merge with the Light of their Higher Self and either take what they need and return, or share what they have learned from life and stay.

'Take another look and see if you notice a difference between the motes, shall we call them souls?'

Dorothy: 'Some, I am not sure most, but some have golden tails.'

Librarian: 'That is not a tail it is the golden cord that attaches them to life, those are the souls still attached to a body and to life. The ones without the "tail" are returning home.'

Dorothy: 'There's a peace and serenity here that is very, very profound, surely if it's the library of souls there would be more distress?'

Librarian: 'Why?'

Dorothy: 'Well death is always sad, sometimes traumatic, sometimes drawn out, you're losing your loved ones.'

Librarian: 'I can see why you would think that way, but now think about the moment of death itself. Perhaps a release from pain and suffering as the soft gentle enfolding of darkness quickly gives way to a gentle Light and to the whispering of those who went before.

'Your soul knows it is going home, and at that moment, even though it may have forgotten throughout its life, it remembers. It remembers where it came from, the Love that sent it forth and although the grief of those it is leaving behind may pull it back, it also experiences the sense of wholeness that returning home offers.'

Dorothy: 'You make it sound so blissful, but people often fear dying throughout their whole lifetimes.'

Librarian: 'Well, perhaps that is a good thing in one way.'

Dorothy: 'Why?'

Librarian: 'To fear the end of your life serves as a reminder that there is a purpose to life and that it is finite. It's all very well being a soul in the Spirit realms learning what you can in the temples of knowledge, sitting at the feet of the Masters and learning about Creation. But, there is no experience to be found in the Spirit realms, knowledge yes, but experience no.

'You know nothing of contrast, neither hot nor cold, pain or pleasure, or how love can be absent or withdrawn.'

Dorothy: 'What do you mean by that?'

Librarian: 'In Spirit all is Love, you exist in a field of Love, in life you have to find love and it's different, no less intense or important, but different.'

Dorothy: 'Different how, Love is Love is it not?'

Librarian: 'Spiritual Love is unconditional, but it is also unsentimental. You cannot earn it, nor lose it, you cannot bargain with it, or disappoint it, but you can turn away from it if, in your soul being, you are in pain and want solitude.

'Earthly love is tested in other ways and is experienced at deep and psychological levels. It has many forms; romantic love, the love for a child or a vulnerable person or animal, the love of self and the world in which you live. A spiritual Love, a Love of a Higher Being, whatever your faith might be, or even your love of free will and self-determination, even a love of believing there is nothing to believe in.'

Dorothy: 'Is the source of spiritual Love and the source of temporal love the same?'

Librarian: 'It is yes, it is the distortions of life and the impact of freewill that make it narrower on Earth and the blindness of mankind to the Love that is all around them. I am thinking here of the Love from nature in particular, almost ignored on your Earth at this time, taken for granted, plundered and almost defeated. Mankind act as if they are wearing blinkers seeing only what they have created, blind to that subtle Light that surrounds and exudes from every living thing. They have forgotten that the Love of the Creator not only made life possible and maintains it, a Love that is constantly renewed from a Source that is infinite.'

Dorothy: 'I feel fear when you speak this way, for I feel inadequate to the task of living harmonising with that Love, with nature and with my fellow man. However strong this fear is, however much my conscience tells me we are standing on the brink, I cannot see a solution. I shrivel up inside at the scale of the task and the rampant destruction of the modern world. I see no alternative and I see no solution, and that scares me.'

Librarian: 'That is why you're here and if you look around you, you will see you are not alone in asking these questions and working through your fear of the Light. Although the Light is currently cowled by the actions of mankind, it is the Light that will provide the answers once it has penetrated the clouds of despair.'

Dorothy: *I look around and I see thousands of other souls listening to this same voice, imbibing the Light that is there and creating this sea of peace that feels ancient, indestructible and all knowing. I am one molecule, one soul, surrounded by an infinite number of souls slowly drinking in Light and fortitude. It lifts my spirits to see this, to see I am not alone. Then I hear it, the Aum, the seabed, the portal back to Earth and I realise I have stepped out of time and perhaps should return now.*

Librarian: 'No, listen again and stay a while, for it is important to move slowly between these realities and not to seek instant solutions to problems that you alone cannot solve. It is no good cutting off from the sea of Light and taking your portion with you without realising that your fragment of Light is essential to the whole. There are times when this seabed, as you called in, needs the presence of men and women, just the presence, not their solutions, or their guilt but their presence. For then Spirit and man are united, and the Light of Spirit can merge with the energy of the earth and gain the power to affect the earth itself. If mankind do not reach out for Spirit we are powerless to act in the temporal realm. So, when you ask what you can do, then this is it; pause, let the Light and peace fill you and stay awhile in the Realm of Light and believe in it.'

The network of Light

Dorothy: 'Aum. I believe in the Light.'

Librarian: 'Shalom to you this day, peace be with you.'

Dorothy: 'Why shalom, I'm not Jewish?'

Librarian: 'It means peace be with you and it is a greeting that evokes peace, it surpasses any religion or faith. Speak the word peace now out loud and what does it evoke?'

Dorothy: 'You're right, I do feel peace settling when I say the word.'

Librarian: 'Words can be vessels for the Light and, as you know, they can be the greatest saboteurs of the Light also. They can open the doors to peace and Love as surely as they can slam those doors shut and leave the listener shivering in their icy wake.'

Dorothy: 'Is this why you are a Librarian because you love words?'

Librarian: 'No, I love life and this is a library of lives, a library of experiences, stories and learning that weaves through eternity like the underground network of tree roots in a vast forest. Look around you, what do you see?'

Dorothy: 'I am standing on a network of Light, rivulets of Light stretching into the far distance. They all have a golden sheen to them, but colours are flashing along them and through them all the time. Some are thick like the tap roots of magnificent trees, some are fine and delicate and yet miraculously are bearing my weight as they are not embedded in anything as far as I can see.'

Librarian: 'Look again at your body, what weight does it bear?'

Dorothy: 'I don't have a body. Am I just here in my mind?'

Librarian: 'Yes, for you, are of the earth and until it is your time to return home you cannot stay in the Library of Lives for your story is not yet complete and so you need the density of life.'

Dorothy: 'But I can visit, please tell me I can visit?'

Librarian: 'Of course you can visit and explore and ask questions, but it is not an escape hatch, or a lifeboat. What we explore here, together, needs to benefit your life, the lives of those around you and the planet which is your home.'

Dorothy: 'I feel sad when you say that, and I don't know why.'

Librarian: 'I do not know for sure because I have never lived on earth, but I know intimately all the stories of those I care for. I listen intently as they recount their experiences on their return. I enfolded them with my Love through the pain of some recollections, through their regret, their sadness and join in with their celebrations of joy as they unravel the true purpose of the life they had lived.

'I never tire of hearing their stories, of reliving their experiences with them as they engage the multiple dimensions of life in Spirit. The Spirit realm is akin to finding yourself in a hall of mirrors, but with the added dimension of nothing being invisible to it. The tendrils of influence from Spirit are just as bright as the bows and arrows of life. The physical and the metaphysical are united in unraveling the purpose, the karma, and the learning.

'I imagine that experiencing the beauty and expansiveness of this place, even for one second, must be moving, even challenging, especially if it unwraps those memories of home buried deep within you at your birth.'

Dorothy: 'I can feel the expansiveness as physically as if I was experiencing heat from a radiator. As much as the network of Light beneath me holds me steady, above me a canopy of Lights stretches far beyond my vision, all interlaced and with a beauty that is not just visible but is visceral. There are places where the canopy rises high into the atmosphere containing universes themselves, temples of learning, holographic gardens of peace and tranquility, all shimmering with Light and communication.

'I see that in each place where are leaf might be there are spirals of Light flickering and spinning all the time, there are buds nestled between the spirals, each one pulsating with life, but dormant, waiting for its time. Some of these spirals are magnificent in their splendour, always carrying one primary colour, often jewel like, but with other colours flashing and shimmering like shoals of fish in the tropical seas.

'The imagery is potent, mesmerising, and I ask myself why? Surely imagination can conjure up anything at all, it does not make it real nor important.'

Librarian: 'Then there's something else that makes this more than a flight of fancy. What is it, what is mesmerising?'

Dorothy: 'The implicate order and harmony that I experience, for that is what exudes the peace. It is like watching ants, or bees around their hive, everything with its place and its purpose and that exudes a beauty beyond the visual because it points to the very process of Creation itself. That great carpet of potential that was rolled out with its pattern invisibly imprinted waiting for life to fill in the colour, shape, and meaning.

'I sense you are nodding and even smiling, but I cannot see you.'

Librarian: 'Well you seem to be seeing and sensing a great deal, some of it, may I say, is quite profound, but I would expect no less from one who has travelled so far to get here. How would you have me look?'

Dorothy: 'I have wondered that myself, I hesitate to apply a stereotype to you of an aged man with wild hair and a long flowing beard, especially as you tell me you have never lived. Doesn't that mean you can take whatever form you wish?'

Librarian: 'You are right that is my gift, but my gift is to appear not as I wish but as my charges can accept me. If that for you is a man in a long flowing robe, with wild hair and long beard, then that is how you will see me. But that is not all I am, for I can be in the eyes of a tramp you pass by in the street, or a newborn child, or a person who is being abused by life itself. For I have lived, in my mind, the lives of all these people and many, many more just as you have in your soul body and that experience touches us all and teaches us all.'

...

'You have returned, does this mean you have questions?'

Dorothy: 'Yes, you say I have travelled far to reach this place, but isn't everyone's journey the same length? There is one journey is there not, from birth to death?'

I feel the ground beneath me shiver and quake as a laugh like a thunderstorm erupting in my imagination that softens into small tinkling quakes of mirth. There is a pause.

Librarian: 'Look around you Dorothy and then look within you, what do you see?'

Dorothy: 'I look up at the tinkling branches, at the spirals of all different sizes and colours and hues. I see some shimmering with a pearlescent gold, some complete with ruby red and sapphire blue spinning gently in a *(non-existent)* breeze. I see spirals that are grey in places, or even black spinning hardly at all, hanging like dead leaves waiting for a winter storm. Spirals are cavorting with one another or moving with speed and surety into hidden bays, or shelves, or goodness knows what.

'I see the winged beings carrying some, my eyes accustomed now to their tiny golden forms and fluttering silver wings, as they move between the lines of

9

moving souls to their destination. All silent, all knowing where they are headed, all compliant with this natural and beautiful order.

'The tiniest spirals are often the most beautiful, they are always iridescent and wave about in the breeze in a gentle rhythm as if they are listening to lullabies sung by angels. The largest spirals are the busiest with visitors and energies moving around them, almost as if they are passing out books to visiting souls. Perhaps they are, perhaps they are the ones telling their stories to those who will listen.

'I look again and see beneath the magnificent trunks of Light small pockets of the leaf buds, gently pulsating with a soft Light. It is as if someone has collected them and placed them gently in baskets which nestle in the protection of the knurled tap roots. I look again and see that there is indeed Light flowing from the leaf buds to the tap roots and back again.'

Librarian: 'I see your eyes are growing accustomed to this place, and as they do what do you see repeated here?'

Dorothy: 'I see similar shapes, but not sizes, similar patterns, but varied through colour and speed of movement. I sense things constantly changing, the whole panorama is impressionistic and ethereal. I want to capture the images and make them recognisable and yet, I don't want to capture them at all for that would be like catching a bird in flight and crushing its life force.'

Librarian: 'Now think of your life, of the people you know and have met, your family and your friends, would you describe their lives as similar to yours or different?'

Dorothy: 'Different.'

Librarian: 'Then why would there be only one journey between life and death? That would be boring would it not if all seven billion incarnated souls trod the same path to this place — let alone the billions that have come before and are yet to follow.

'Look around you again at the lines of Light connecting this Realm to all other Realms. See the highways, the country lanes, the footpaths, the ocean tides, the bridges and yes, even the roundabouts of Light, for sometimes people think their time has come and they are turned back.

'Look again at the single footpaths that have mountains within them, valleys and wild water streams to ford, those are the spiritual paths, the ones where you walk alone in life, but not in Spirit. The ones where you are accompanied and carried in invisible arms out of the crevasses you fall into. Where Spirit waits for you to return from the cul-de-sacs of life, gently waiting with absolute patience, even unto your deathbed, for you to return to the path and walk once again in that pale Light they scatter before you.'

Dorothy: 'Is that what has brought me here?'

Librarian: 'In your case, yes it has. Often the route here is more acute, the result of some trauma or distress, but yours has been more meandering, reluctant and hesitant at times, but that means it is rich with learning and the potential to help others.'

Dorothy: 'Huh, it has just felt hard to me, filled with potholes and mistakes and missteps. A legacy of heartbreak in so many ways.'

Librarian: 'But that is like cutting into a wedding cake and proclaiming that the cake is a disaster because it contains marzipan. First you knew there would be a layer of marzipan, but the marzipan is not the cake. The ingredients have been chosen with care, the recipe was good and the baker very proficient. You have one thin layer of something you find distasteful surrounding a perfectly baked cake which was created with Love and which has fed and raised a lovely family and been shared with many. To your credit, you have not discarded the marzipan but eaten your share at, at times, have recognised the skill of the baker and the wisdom of the recipe.'

Dorothy: 'If there are so many pathways, highways and country lanes to this place then why is diversity and difference so feared in life? It is not within nature, so why in mankind?'

Librarian: 'The short answer is freewill, what you see here in the Library of Lives is the immaculate order of Creation fulfilling its purpose in peaceful harmony and that touches your heart, as it does mine. In mankind freewill has become supreme and the inner connection with soul has dimmed as a result.

'If you look again at the highways of Light that lead to this place you will see how many souls now bear the cloak of regret. I have been here since the beginning of time, so I can see the difference between "now" in your timescale and "before".'

Dorothy: *He's right, as I look again I see that although the highway is in bright light many of the souls are not, they carry a speck of something else, like a seed that they have yet to plant. As I look to the tinnier paths, the footpaths and the country lanes I see less of this dimness and more Light within the souls that are moving along, even though the paths themselves have a gentler Light.*

Your beautiful soul

Walk with me, talk with me,
I sense your woes,
for wherever you travel,
I go where you go.

We're inextricably bound
beyond earth and space.
I'm the guardian of purpose
the Source of your grace.

When your heart it is open,
Light and life interweave,
in a pattern so complex
it's hard to conceive.

That this pattern encodes
the path of Creation,
person by person,
and nation by nation.

All this is inscribed
in your beautiful soul,
let unraveling its mystery
become your life's goal.

Experiencing the Higher Self

Dorothy: 'Aum ... I believe in the Light.'

Librarian: 'Well this is a pleasure three visits in three days. Shalom to you this cold and frosty morning when all is quiet in your world and peace and nature have the upper hand once again.'

Dorothy: 'Shalom to you. I am finding these visits to be more protracted than my writing can convey, the content of our conversations remains with me throughout my day and fills my dreams.'

Librarian: 'Well, that is in part because your soul remains connected to your Higher Self throughout your life. Often during sleep it seeks guidance, or reassurance, or simply contact with the Spirit realm, but your recollection of those visits will be encoded in the concerns of life. Your Higher Self might be advising you about certain situations, or relationships, and your personality may interpret that as an anxiety dream where you feel fear and seek safety or glimpse someone close to you in a different guise.'

Dorothy: 'So is that what the Library of Lives stores then? Higher Selves, whatever they are?'

Librarian: 'Exactly so, do you remember on your first visit here you imagined being in a library with tomes the height of people, standing on each other's shoulders reaching up beyond your vision?'

Dorothy: 'Yes, I do. I thought what I saw was leather-bound volumes with gold glinting off the titles and the binding. But as I looked closer the hard edges of the books morphed into a wall of Angelic beings all interacting one with another and with the energy forms that glided around them, merging sometimes or just paying a fleeting visit.

'It was charming and it moves me now to think of it, for words hardly do it justice. What I was seeing, and feeling, had two components within it that would normally be contradictory; a sense of ancient, total and complete peace in a state of constant flux and communication. As I conjure up the image again, it has a sense of home about it.'

Librarian: 'You have just described your Higher Self and as you were speaking you felt its presence and that is precious indeed. From your description one tome, is one Being of Light, representing your Higher Self, that nurtures all the lives your Soul has ever lived, all the lessons it has learnt and all the lessons it has yet to learn.

'These imaginary forms are representations of Light, just as I am, presented to you in ways which you can recognise, or interpret. If you follow them, they will open your mind to the vast Realms beyond life on earth and, perhaps more importantly, to bring to your life the experience of never being alone and of life eternal.'

Dorothy: 'So are these images personal to me? Would another soul visiting this library imagine other details then?'

Librarian: 'Yes, you bring what you know to this place and the Light here constellates around your interests and your need for safety.

'Let's try something ... close your eyes and let yourself float once again into the Light, do not direct, just float.'

Dorothy: 'I am in a pond, the weather is warm and all around me are fishes of every hue and colour, Koi Carp, swimming in crystal clear water. I watch them now diving deeper and deeper as if they are following an underground stream. There are large ones out front swimming strongly and leading the shoal behind them. They are swimming with purpose and leaving rivulets of rainbows in their wake.

'I am no longer present in the pool, but in my mind I am watching them from behind and realise that although we are now in total darkness. Light is all around us, the fish emit a changing palette of colours and it shimmers in the darkness. There is no noise other than the gentle swish of the water as the fish swim, now in total unison.

'The individual fish shapes are now disappearing into a spiral of Light and colour that shimmers before me, pulsating to the sound of my heart and inviting me forward. I hesitate, fearing I might interrupt that upward flow. I feel my body to be heavy and unwieldy, but I step forward anyway and allow myself to be absorbed into the Light which feels peaceful and leaves me feeling rested, as if I have been on a journey.'

Librarian: 'That was an experience of your Higher Self, different to the tomes and the angelic beings, but similar in so many ways. The images are really insignificant, it is the feeling, the inner experience that is important and in that exchange of Light and colour was knowledge, Love and memories, some of which may emerge as the days and nights progress.'

Dorothy: 'How many souls are within each Higher Self?'

Librarian: 'Before I answer that let us explore together your Library of Lives, for within this creation are universal Truths that can applied equally to any other form of representation.

'Return in your mind's eye to your wall of angelic beings, recall that sense of space and inner pathways. See those images as you would a vast library, larger than anything upon your earth, more akin to a night sky. Patterns of light connecting distant stars and galaxies together, seemingly infinite and yet, should you pause at one star, there it is palpable, living, changing, constantly interacting with all the other stars and planets.

'Were you able to communicate with each other that star would have a tale to tell, a story as old as Creation and yet as vibrant as that morning's rain. Its orbit would be intricately balanced with all the other stars and planets, each with their history, purpose, and place.

'That is like your Library of Lives you have connections, corridors of bookshelves, that mirror every aspect of life; science, religion, healing, commerce, governance, philosophy, defence, manufacture, mining, war, peace, education. In fact, they do not just mirror they initiate, for all pathways run through the Vale of Thought, a vast pool of energy from which all thoughts come and to which all thoughts return.

'There is nothing new on the Earth, everything emanates from Spirit, for that is life itself. It is the energy that animates the Soul and enables life. A Truth, I will grant you, that seems impossible to contemplate in a world where freewill reigns supreme and the earth itself has become little more than a repository for the needs and greed of mankind.'

Dorothy: 'Is that why I imagined Temples of Learning and Holographic universes within the canopy of leaves?'

Librarian: 'Yes, that is what you saw in your mind's eye, structures of Light where the scientists and astrophysicists collaborate, far in advance of mankind. Places where souls learn by bringing their earthly knowledge to bear on the problems facing mankind. Crystalline forms created through thought alone where knowledge can be tested and shared and communicated throughout the Spirit world, where Realm upon Realm learn from each other and from returning souls.'

Dorothy: 'Is that why I saw layer upon layer stretching upwards.'

Librarian: 'Yes, you sensed the progression of Light, the differences in vibration that separate the Realms, the desire within souls to become more refined, closer to the Source and to move from individuality into the collective.'

Dorothy: 'So how many souls are there?'

Librarian: 'How would you calculate that number?'

Dorothy: 'I guess I would begin by the number of people on the planet, around seven billion I think and then add the other billion or so who are pregnant, so that's eight plus billion to start with. Or at least it was before the pandemic.

'I have no idea how anyone can estimate all the past populations. I can find estimates of between 107 – 113 billion people, that's an enormous number of souls and begs the question of how big the Spirit world must be to accommodate that many souls? One reference I have seen says there are 15 dead people for every person living.'

Librarian: *Laughing.* 'Well hold on to your hat then, for this will surprise you. There is one Soul.'

Dorothy: 'How is that possible? As I look around the Library I see a vast expanse of knowledge and Light and constant comings and goings. There are the new arrivals weary and tired, channels of learning and endeavour stretching further than I can see, or even imagine. I see Hierarchies and sense Masters walking among the gathered souls, true each one is infinitesimal, but pulsating with so much life.

'Surely that amount of life, knowledge, and experience cannot be contained within one soul?'

Librarian: 'That is mainly because your interpretation of Soul is individual. I am not being critical here because man tends to see things in his, or her, own image rather than understanding that every person is part of a collective and all individual aspects of soul originated from one Soul.

'There is one Soul that fragmented and each person bears one fragment throughout one life, whether that life is one day or one hundred years long. Every fragment has one opportunity for life, not all take them, but when all the learning that the one Soul desires has been accrued then the collective will reconstitute.'

Dorothy: 'What happens to any karma that has been created throughout those billions of lives?'

Librarian: 'That will have to be assuaged too, for what is created in life has to be assuaged in life and the personalities involved have to play their part in that.'

Dorothy: 'While you were speaking I was back in my forest, the canopy of leaves above me, the magnificent trees all around and scuttling at my feet were the tiny creatures scavenging for food.'

Librarian: 'Ah yes, the animals, let us not forget the animals, the natural world, that garden that was created for the Soul to learn in.'

Dorothy: 'Do animals and plants also have souls then?'

Librarian: 'They are all part of Soul, but they have group Souls, not the individual fragments that rest in individual personalities. Each species has a Group Soul and within that Group is the potential for evolution and development, particularly in the domesticated animals who know the love of a human being.

'If your eyes has attuned a little more you would have seen images of beloved dogs, cats, and horses visiting the returning souls as they nestled into their Higher Selves for the first time. It is heart-warming to see them greet their previous owners before returning to the Group Soul of their species. When you next visit look closely, you will not see the detail, but you will see sparks of pleasure and recognition rise from the returning soul as they see their beloved animal and feel its delight at their reunion.'

Dorothy: 'Many people believe that you can be reincarnated as an animal. If animals have Group Souls and people have individual fragments of soul that does not seem so possible.'

Librarian: That is right, although they are all part of Soul mankind and the natural world have different pathways and Soul structures. The natural world is a world of instinct and following Sacred Law, the world of mankind is a path of self responsibility and freewill.'

Dorothy: 'Your answer has within it the same stillness that I experience in the library, a steadying, not of knowing at a personal level, but of being in the presence of knowing, of certainty amidst movement, change, and flux. Thank you.'

Librarian: 'You are welcome. Like the magnificent trees in your forest there are pillars of Truth that hold up the canopy of Light and bring peace to the heart.'

Gentleness

When you speak of the Source,
you are speaking of me,
that essence of Love
that allows you to be.

To be what you are
and to know that it's true,
that you come from Love
and that Love's within you.

So be gentle my love,
to yourself and this world,
for within gentle movements
you'll see Love unfurl.

So be kind to yourself,
and to all those you know,
for within words of kindness
that Love it will grow.

And then every soul,
from the first to the last,
will be infused with a Love
that cannot be surpassed.

The action of the Light

Dorothy: 'Aum ... I believe in the Light.'

Librarian: 'And indeed you do, and already this morning it and you have been busy at work.'

Dorothy: 'Well yes, I thought people who have never met me might need a context and a sense of where these words are — I was going to say coming from, but that's not right — being captured as they fall.'

Librarian: 'This was a good example of a joint initiative, you went to bed thinking that way and overnight between your soul and Higher Self a format started to emerge and then in the early morning the words flowed and you caught them in your net.

'I liked that image, but I would also like to point to the learning that took place. How many times have you recounted your story about feeling alone as a schoolgirl?'

Dorothy: 'Hardly at all until I did the Grief Recovery training and even now perhaps less than thirty times. It was not until much later in life I even considered it as important.'

Librarian: 'How detailed is your memory?'

Dorothy: 'Very, I can see where I was standing, what I was wearing and feeling and what had led up to it. I can recall the weather and the release that making that statement, even silently to myself, evoked. I remember walking into school with my head held high even after realising that, "anyone I could expect to love me doesn't, so now I am on my own."

'What surprised me years later was that my mother who had shouted the words, "I don't love you either", in response to me saying the same thing to her, remembered that fight. Out of all the fights we had, she remembered and regretted that one, but neither of us mentioned it again until years later.'

Librarian: 'Then you were right to have classed it as a turning point. Memories that detailed are imprinted on the soul itself, that type of profound experience, in your case experiencing both despair and release, are often invaluable in later life. You grew up instinctively knowing that if you suffered the despair release might follow and this forbearance has held you in good stead.

'What was also of note, for me, was the action of the Light in illuminating a link for you between your sense of the impermanence of life and feeling alone at such an early age — at least within your culture. Of course, I know that this had a negative impact too, for you harboured a fear of further loss and abandonment for many years. But I wanted you to see that this morning, like a brain creating new neural pathways, your ability to access the wisdom of your soul when revisiting events from your past enables the Light to fill those events. This will encourage you to uncover the learning and their value to your development.'

Dorothy: 'Yes I see that and it's true I had not considered that event before this morning as anything more than being responsible for my rather fierce attachment to independence, which also had a negative impact in later life.'

Slowing down

Librarian: 'So you're a little flat this morning?'

Dorothy: 'Yes, I'm finding little enthusiasm for the year ahead, apart from the arrival of our granddaughter, and I am feeling sad.'

Librarian: 'Let's explore the sadness then is it personal, or collective?'

Dorothy: 'Both, my partner returned from his walk this morning having passed all night parties and collected up empty bottles from them and in the current circumstances that just seems so reckless and selfish. Almost a thousand people a day are dying and I am finding every excuse not to leave home, but on the other hand I am badly missing my freedom and any sense of agency within the world.'

Librarian: 'Every day you work with the Light and send prayers to those in need and to the earth too, is that not enough?'

Dorothy: 'It's intangible, almost — and I am sorry to say this — aspirational. An act of faith that at this current time seems foolhardy at best, delusional at worst, as people continue acting in ways that are actually deadly at the moment without, it seems, a care in the world for others. I want to cry.'

Librarian: 'Then do, for it is the absence of tears that is enabling people to continue acting with such disregard for others and for the earth itself.

'Spirit has no wish for mankind to suffer more than they need to assuage the karma that has been accrued. Change cannot be avoided, here, dry your eyes for a moment and walk with me.

'See yourself sitting in a courtyard garden in the midst of a large metropolis. The sun is shining and there is a sense of activity all around you. You are more elderly than you are now and frail, your movements are slow but deliberate. You delight in the beauty of this garden, the scent of the flowers, the bees, and insects, the shade of the trees that you have known since you were a child. Etched in your surroundings are memories of your parents, your children, and grandchildren, and there is a serenity that fills you and surrounds you.

'You place on the table at your side an empty cup that you have been sipping from and slowly rise to take your morning walk. The air is clear because it rained in the night and as you close the ornate gates behind you, you take a deep breath which fills your lungs with the scent of jasmine and roses.

'As you walk in the streets of your neighbourhood you are greeted by familiar faces and the whole area is buzzing with quiet commerce, but there is something different and you can't quite put your finger on it. Everybody seems to be moving at a slower pace, and there are smiles on the faces of those in the street and in the shops. You are struck by how the very elderly, like yourself, are mixing with the young and how everyone seems more relaxed with time to exchange a few words, with their brothers and sisters.

'It is all gentle, that is the change, gentleness seems to have come down with the nighttime shower and embraced all generations.'

Dorothy: 'Thank you that was lovely.'

Librarian: 'Now, you may ask why did I take you on that journey, on the surface that scenario is far away from your own life? Well, it is not, for the changes that need to come about are universal, they are for every country and every generation and they will bring about a better quality of life for all.

'But it is in the slowing down that you create the space for change to occur. In this meditation the slowing down was due to old age, but there are other interventions that lead to slowing down and illness and an interruption in commerce are but two. People change because they have to, not because they want to. Think of yourself and your writing would this be happening if you were still able to work?'

Dorothy: 'No, I would not think of it as a valuable use of my time, nor at all helpful in paying the bills and that has been my priority for so many years.'

Librarian: 'Of course it has and rightfully so as you and your partner have been raising a family. There is value in working, I am not decrying that, but the collective quality of life and the importance of community have been neglected for so many years as the value of life has been measured in purely commercial terms.

'That has left a legacy of imposing walls and high fences around not just homesteads but people and generations too. A legacy of self-protection not mutual trust and a belief that anything goes, hence the partying in the midst of a pandemic which you consider reckless, while others claim to be their birthright.'

Dorothy: 'I know you are right and your words have settled my heart and brought me some hope, but I know for so many people the concept of slowing down is terrifying for they have nothing to fall back on.'

Librarian: 'I know that what you mean by that statement is that they will be unable to survive financially and feed their families and, of course, that concern is legitimate as things currently stand. But I would ask you to consider two other things; firstly most people need less not more and certainly the planet needs some people to curb their consumption quite significantly.

'Secondly, perhaps surprisingly, the greatest lack at this time is the poverty in belief, or faith, or an inner Light that makes people feel they have a value, that they belong to something greater and that their life has meaning. This lack is the fuel behind conspicuous consumption and selfishness, and is the heartbreak most people do their best to avoid.

'That is why I said at the beginning "allow your tears to fall" for if more people could allow their sadness the gentleness you saw and felt in the meditation would be within reach.'

Dorothy: 'Thank you, that has felt like a journey and has left me feeling settled, although not exactly hopeful as I am aware that the changes that are needed are so subtle they are easily ignored or dismissed.'

Librarian: 'This is the outworking of the Golden Age, the influence of the Archangel Michael and the Christos. It is imperative that this beautiful pearlescent Light which brings Love, compassion, gentleness, and healing to this world and everything upon it breaks through the carapace of greed and ignorance that currently threatens the very future of mankind.

'What is a source of great sadness in the Spirit realms is that most of humanity is blind to the infinite beauty that is freely available, that could fill their every waking moment, their relationships, and their hopes and dreams. No one in Spirit decries the everyday concerns and worries that preoccupy humanity, but they weep when what is so small by comparison consumes and overwhelms the very energy that would bring release, not to some, but to all.'

Purpose

Your purpose is the seed that's planted
long before you enter life.
Exquisite in its form and function,
its perfume is the balm to strife.

Allow its scent to fill your senses,
shine a light on footsteps planned,
bring to you the Light of Spirit.
So take its proffered, loving, hand.

For then your journey will have meaning,
both the darkness and the light,
for as purpose blooms within you,
there'll be far less black and white.

Imagination or inspiration?

Dorothy: 'Shalom to you. I am hesitant this morning about putting finger to keyboard because I don't want to be follow my imagination and create topics. I want to discover what is beyond me.'

Librarian: 'Shalom to you my beloved sister and although your concerns are real, they are of no of concern to me. Where would we have been yesterday were it not for your imagination? The detail of the garden, the scents, and the hues of the plants were, you might say, a joint creation, but it was a creation that was guided and which I know you followed and did not lead. Indeed, there were times when as your fingers were writing up your images your rational mind was asking, "Where is this going?" But without waiting for a reply that question floated away and you continued capturing the words.

'Now, there is an interesting point I would like to follow that arises from your initial statement about discovering things beyond yourself. When you conceive of the Spirit realms where do you envisage them? In the clouds, above your Earth in some place called heaven?'

Dorothy: 'Well yes, to a large extent yes. I do imagine the Earth surround by Realms of Light, bands of colour, that house the Spirit realms. I also know, or have read, that this separation is man made and that the Spirit realms are integral to the Earth and life itself, but instinctively, I think of the sky and the universe beyond. It is a very common expression to speak of a loved one who has passed as looking down from above.'

Librarian: 'When in a little while you close your computer and go about your daily life do you still feel my presence?'

Dorothy: 'Yes I do, increasingly I do, particularly in my quiet moments or when I am musing on something we have spoken about.'

Librarian: 'And at that moment do I feel any more distant than I do now?'

Dorothy: 'No, the quality of contact is just the same, but there is something different in how I react to any spontaneous contact.'

Librarian: 'What is different?'

Dorothy: 'There is more of a tendency in me to discount the spontaneous inspiration — and really I am thinking about this for the first time — because when I sit and deliberately make contact I consciously suspend my disbelief.'

Librarian: 'So to record our encounters, you have to actively overcome a degree of disbelief each time?'

Dorothy: 'That both sounds harsher than I experience it but also true, in that there is a process of acceptance and curiosity that I engage to speak with you and trust what I am hearing. After all you are not speaking in the voice of another, you are speaking in my voice, using the same language and even the same inflections, so I am effectively dialoging with myself within my head. There are many people in mental hospital because they hear voices.'

Librarian: 'That is all very true and what is key is your ability and your willingness to trust and that has been hard won. When we first spoke, I acknowledged your long journey and you felt I was almost mocking you, for you discount the lessons along your path as mistakes or failures that evoke shame. But each lesson was a stepping stone to the degree of trust that now comes naturally to you.

'You have learnt many things along your pathway and they have woven together into your ability to sit quietly and yet fill with the Light of Spirit. You have learnt to discern one voice over another, not by its volume, but by its gentleness and the impact on yourself and those around you. This is because in the past you have turned away and set your face against Spirit in the belief that you had been abandoned by God Itself. You have felt the burrs of self flagellation and self recrimination burn into your skin night after night, and suffered seemingly unstoppable tears of grief and regret flowing until they could flow no more.'

Dorothy: 'Please stop, you make it sound almost noble, but it wasn't. It was a mess and there is a trail of destruction on that pathway that can never be rebuilt. There are opportunities lost, friendships shattered, and a mountain of regrets that I worry will accompany me home and plague me into eternity.'

Librarian: 'Now that is where we differ. To follow your analogy, the destruction that you see littering your pathway has within it the material qualities that are serving you well now. They enable you to have an inner dialogue with your soul without you, or anyone else, questioning your sanity — well not in earshot anyway.

'The destruction was necessary. I would concede not all of it, but the majority was essential, not only for you personally, but for your soul to be able to expand to fulfil its purpose in this life. It was also, and this may surprise you, orchestrated by your soul. What you consider to be mistakes and failures your soul regards as learning opportunities either taken or ignored. Lessons designed to help you fulfil your purpose and your promise to God that you made in your soul body before you were born.'

Dorothy: 'My heart knows that what you are saying is true because I am — proud is maybe too strong a word — relieved that I did not walk away, but I do not feel entirely settled or secure. I carry within a sense of loss that has not gone away, I have just learnt to live with it. I am also nervous about deluding myself again and so even writing this is challenging.

'I have just reread your reply above and there is something else that I battle with and that is your suggestion that I, this personality called Dorothy, is important enough to have made any kind of promise to God. That this one speck of sand on a seashore stretching into infinity could be important at all.

'Now, I know that this is the flip side of my past self-styled belief that I could make a valuable contribution to a spiritual venture — a belief that was swiftly cut down by my travelling companions, even by God Itself. So regaining some degree of balance is not easy as there is a spectrum between worthless and important that I can still travel daily, if not hourly.'

Librarian: 'You have expertly taken us back to whether Spirit is separate from yourself floating on some distant cloud, or an inherent part of you that is present at all times, even the very worst of times. A presence that needs your permission and attention to be visible, conscious and present in life.'

Dorothy: 'What do you mean by permission?'

Librarian: 'I mean the act of tuning your consciousness into that still small voice of calm and disengaging your critical mind long enough to allow the words to settle in your heart. The voice of Spirit always carries Love and peace within it, it does not direct or override freewill, that remains sacrosanct. You directed the conversation this morning, and indeed every morning, for as I follow so I lead and as you lead so I follow.

'There is no separation, your soul is within every cell of your body and every person is part of Creation and able to create. No beach would exist without grains of sand, but just as the sea moulds the shoreline, so every person both affects Spirit and is affected by it. There is a spiral of mutual learning that can never be broken and occurs within one atom of space.'

Later that morning ...

Dorothy: 'As if to prove a point, as I was stripping beds it occurred to me that whatever took place between myself and my fellow travellers must have been two-way and not as personal as it felt at the time.'

Librarian: 'I think you already know that the answer to this is in the affirmative and I have chosen my word carefully here. It is an affirmation of the wisdom that has accrued from what many would describe as devastating. It is only because of your tenacity, born from the purpose of your soul, that that wisdom has accrued and been released through the action of Light.

'Intense relationships, both positive and negative, usually bear the hallmarks of karma and in a spiritual setting that is almost guaranteed. So, every conflict is mutually beneficial, you might say, providing valuable lessons and opportunities for the Light to heal the divisions. In a spiritual setting, you may well have souls in their last incarnation — before completing the purpose of their Higher Self — and that means the imperative to assuage any karma is pressing down on all parties.

'Unfortunately, this can have the perverse effect of making the situations seem intractable because the stakes are so high for all concerned and even, in some cases, beyond those individuals or that setting. It is exactly because these lessons are so precious that they can prove so hard to accept, and that is a common paradox that litters the spiritual path and assails those upon it. It leads to unfounded accusations of maliciousness and jealousy which scar those involved and which, while in life, can never be truly forgiven or forgotten.'

Surrendering to the spiritual

Dorothy: 'Shalom.'

Librarian: 'Shalom to you this day and may I say I feel the disturbance in the surrounding peace. Is there something you wish to share?'

Dorothy: 'This does not seem a good use of your time.'

Librarian: *Laughs.* 'Time is not something I am short of, or bothered by, and in any case do you think your concerns are invisible to me outside our times of contact? Do you want to frame in words what is bothering you today?'

Dorothy: 'I read a scathing article earlier this morning on how spiritual people are, or can feel, smug and superior to others and have huge egos while proclaiming just the opposite, and it affected me.'

Librarian: 'How did it affect you?'

Dorothy: 'At first I was dismissive, thinking that the writer didn't know what she was talking about, that trying to follow a spiritual path was anything but easy or inclined to create a feeling of smugness. But then I wondered if there was truth in her statement about compassion making non-judgemental people appear smug to others, perhaps even condescending as if they are above it all.'

Librarian: 'How did that make you feel?'

Dorothy: 'Sad with a tinge of anger, but the anger was hiding despair, I think.'

Librarian: 'Why the despair?'

Dorothy: 'I guess it's the impossibility of relating to people on a deeper level and of the cynical judgement that is so rife in this world at this time.'

Librarian: 'What would your answer be to her should you ever meet?'

Dorothy: 'That engaging with spirituality is difficult, fraught with danger, self judgement and fear, not least of being called a hypocrite. It's an ongoing process which involves a few steps forward but many more backwards, all blindfolded, and with little tangible feedback, except for the peace growing within and your ability to turn back to it when things get tough.

'That, with this increase in inner peace, when you find yourself in the presence of obvious distress there is a desire to share what you have come to understand, or accept. But even as you share, you fear that the Light is too personal or fragile to flourish outside the sanctuary of your heart. You know better than anyone that progress is fragile and attempting to help another may be naive or delusional, but you do it anyway and that act of courage is worthy of praise not ridicule.'

Librarian: 'I feel the anger and the despair in what you say and that saddens me because your world at this time needs compassion and the suspense of judgement more than at any time before. You have considered her statement from within yourself, a person trying to first understand themselves and then help others and that is what I asked of you, but what of the writer, what might be affronting her?'

Dorothy: 'I am always uncomfortable answering questions like this because it tends to put the blame on the critic and could therefore prevent me, or anyone else, looking for the truth within the criticism.'

Librarian: 'This, I'm afraid, is partly due to the legacy you carry of having had such a critical mother. Rather than evaluating any criticism as saying something about the critic as well as yourself, or the topic, you strive to accept the whole criticism as valid, as it is easier for you to accept criticism than praise.'

Dorothy: *Raises her eyes to heaven.*

Librarian: 'Now indulge me … in the early days of your spiritual journey what put you off spiritual settings and encounters, and here I am not talking about your home background, but about the people you met and interacted with?'

Dorothy: 'There were people who seemed to invade my personal space, they would assume knowledge about me, often talk in platitudes and act in ways that were contrary to how I expected them to behave as so-called spiritual people.'

Librarian: 'So they did not meet your expectations and were invasive. Might you have described them as self-satisfied?'

Dorothy: 'I suppose so, yes, and, to be fair, acting as if they were "above it all". It was as if life did not touch them at all, they had a quick comeback for everything, even those things that I know caused them grief. They appeared to me to be disingenuous, and so I was mistrustful.'

Librarian: 'Are those not the same criticisms that the author was levelling at all spiritual people?'

Dorothy: 'Yes they are.'

Librarian: 'So what caused your distress and anger then if you have felt those things yourself and, dare I say it, still feel those things even now?'

Dorothy: 'It reminded me of my fear and reluctance when engaging with spiritual groups for the first time as an adult. My mother had used spirituality as an escape hatch from life and so as a child I was wary of it and possibly angry at how she used her beliefs and implied threats to try — unsuccessfully — to control me.'

Librarian: 'If you recognise that your own life history fuels your reactions, then why not this author's? There is also the question of why, given your own history, you engaged with spirituality at all?'

Dorothy: 'I can see where you are going with this ... I was drawn to spiritual settings because that has been, and is, important for my soul in this life. Perversely, that importance also increased my fear as a child, and substantial reluctance as an adult, to engage with spirituality. Perhaps I knew instinctively it would require me to surrender my freewill at some point and so I became belligerent as a defence.'

Librarian: *Laughing.* 'There's very little I would disagree within your self-analysis, except to be a little kinder on you than you have been on yourself. There is within you, and within most other people, a conflict between the needs of the soul — in your case to follow a spiritual path, for shorthand — and the personality.

'So when you say that you, Dorothy, instinctively knew that engaging with spirituality would require the surrender of freewill it is not entirely accurate. It was your soul that knew this, and the conflict that you experienced was with your personality that had used its freewill to survive your childhood and to start out alone at quite a tender age.

'It is more difficult, you might say, to relinquish something that is seen as a birthright in your world, especially when it is the very quality that has taken you to the places and people that you were destined to love and work with. You have much to thank your freewill for, more than most, and so you should forgive yourself for eventually facing down that inner conflict in favour of your soul.

'Who knows what inner conflict your author may be facing and whether she will have the courage to face it down too. But it matters not because if it matters to her soul then the opportunity to do so will be presented time and time again and if not in this life then in the next and the one after that.'

The embers of remembrance

There's meeting, and there's knowing
and they're not quite the same.
Some people are familiar,
some no more than a name.

It's neither their demeanour,
their appearance, or their class.
There's something in that meeting
that you know is built to last.

There is no need for questions,
there's acceptance straight away.
And in that fleeting moment
distinctions fade away.

There's a mutual recognition
that you cannot quite explain.
But you know that you look forward
to seeing them again.

But it's not your eyes that capture
the truth of who they are,
it's a soul to soul connection
that all of mankind share.

These are the jewels in your heart,
that accompany you back home,
the embers of remembrance
reminding you you're not alone.

The power of thought

Dorothy: 'Shalom to you this day. It is the first day back to work for so many lucky enough to have work to return to as the pandemic is really severe in this country now. I do feel for those people waking up this morning without employment, or any means to pay their bills, and feel so grateful for my situation.'

Librarian: 'I know from your earlier meditation with your partner that you also thought about the things you wish to bring to me today.'

Dorothy: 'I do, but because I have been musing on two different things I feel I have to choose one over the other, or to ignore both and come with an empty mind.'

Librarian: 'Your mind is never really empty for it is always in touch with the Vale of Thought where energies flash like the Koi Carp in your pond evoking ideas, concerns and solutions all the time. So, I would argue that these the concerns floated to the surface because your mind was already alert to our assignation, shall we say.

'In fact you might say that were you to engage your freewill at this point and prioritise what you bring then you are placing yourself above your soul and therefore God.'

Dorothy: 'That's a bit harsh isn't it, our time together is precious and so it has to be used wisely.'

Librarian: 'As you know, I have all the time in the world, so what would be an unwise use of it in your view?'

Dorothy: 'I don't know really, I was reacting to your statement about me putting myself above God, or my soul, as I would never knowingly do that.'

Librarian: 'Beloved one you do it all the time, everybody does, you are in life and subject to its pull and its push, and at this time that push is away from Spirit and towards the temporal. I am not saying the temporal has no value, of course it does, or there would be no life on Earth, but it has become overinflated at the expense of everything else, not least the peace in people's hearts.

'I think that might bring us to the topics that were on your mind?'

Dorothy: 'During the meditation I was thinking of how a single image can change everything for me in a way that perhaps words cannot. My example is that over the weekend I was invited to voice a remote healing and group meditation that we do at a specified time. Normally, my partner speaks, but this time he asked me to. Instead of listing everyone in need of healing I saw the image of a snowflake and once the Light established itself at its centre it immediately travelled down all its branches. As it travelled it created new channels like water creates rivulets, and reached everyone in need. On that occasion, I did use names because I have associated names with the transmission of direct healing, but this morning just seeing the image of the snowflake seemed to be enough.

'It also happened when I was struggling to move on from past events. After many years, I saw an image of the key people concerned and there was a sudden spatial shift where they became more distant and that image seemed to release me from my physical embodying of the pain.'

Librarian: 'And, if I may, you were thinking about something more recent, were you not?'

Dorothy: 'Yes, from yesterday's article I recalled an image when she mentioned, "crystal strokers". It made me think of a clip from an old Bond film, a mythical secret agent, where the enemy appears stroking a cat, an image that has become an icon of something evil.'

Librarian: 'I can see how you would think that these two images are separate but, as with the nature of all things they are not, they are connected as they are both illuminating the same errors in thinking.

'The Healing Light that is released during meditation is instant, intelligent and can seek out a need for its presence faster and more accurately than any heat seeking missile. Its release into this world, thanks to you and to many others, is important and needs the human touch, so to speak, to be effective. But it is greater than you and greater than humanity as a whole, so, at your stage of development, a single image that has filled with Light, before imbibing the essential quality of your love, is all that is needed.

'What is not fulfilled in that instantaneous transmission is the very human need to feel valued, thoughtful, compassionate and committed, and I do not decry that at all. If mankind accepted that in order to transmit the Light nothing more is needed than the imbibing of that Light, a belief in it and thought, it would be even harder for them to believe meditation produces any positive benefit.

So, rituals have their place as long as they do not seek to direct, or obscure, the spontaneity of the Light.

'Should mankind ever wake up to the power of thought, then surely what would follow would be a realisation that there must a flip side? If Light and Love can be transmitted instantaneously through thought alone, then surely that is also true of anger, hatred, and prejudice. In your world at this time that realisation could be a great burden. It is, of course, a burden that mankind collectively will have to address at some point because it is the source of the clouds of darkness that currently surround the Earth and weakens the ability of Spirit to assist.'

Dorothy: 'Gosh, that's taken my breath away.'

Librarian: 'I am sorry, but it needs to, not take just your breath away but the breath of mankind. No one alive fully appreciates the collective power of thought, of how the energy of Light, healing and peace can be released by humanity into this earth in an instance and maintained. For they have forgotten that there is a purpose and meaning to life that is way more rewarding than any salary.'

Dorothy: 'I am beginning to see how the "crystal strokers" comment might fit into this. Not only what you were saying yesterday about how our fear and upbringing govern our attitudes to our spirituality, but how easily we can mock and dismiss something that is part of Creation. It is fashionable to knock the healing power of crystals, but not the other life giving and healing aspects of our natural world which we exploit without concern for its conservation. I don't know if she intended to link crystals with evil, but even unconsciously she did, and that speaks more to her fear but also creates one more hurdle she may yet have to overcome. But I have been there myself, so I know how easy it is to be cynical and how difficult it can be to surrender to something so intangible.'

Librarian: 'Indeed, that is a good summary and the reason I said at the beginning that your soul could see the links even when your personality could not. Your body, your soul, your earth, and the Spirit realms are all linked through crystalline structures. Just like your snowflake, these are the lines down which the Light constantly flows bringing knowledge, Love, understanding and peace to your earth and linking the Realms constantly. "As above so below" remember, so one image will link with another and through that the Light will flow down yet another branch, another tributary and out into your world, and for that, may I add, Love thanks you.'

Your soul is a sculptor

The image of your childhood
that floated into view,
was a sad one, this I do know,
because it reminded you.

Of a time when love was absent,
in your household and your heart,
and, although you hardly knew it,
you were being torn apart.

There was betrayal on many levels,
of your childhood most of all,
but as the memories flicker,
it's emptiness that you recall.

That loss became a vessel
that you've carried to this day,
an empty space within you
that has never gone away.

Now, perhaps this will surprise you,
this space serves you everyday,
for it is the chamber that I visit,
to say what I must say.

You see your soul it is a sculptor,
that with care their chisel wields,
to create those inner chambers
that allows Spirit to heal.

Truth & Love

Librarian: 'Beloved one, shalom to you this day and peace be with you. I was with you in your earlier meditation and so I have advance notice, you might say, of what you wish to cover today and I welcome it. Likewise, I am aware that you had something of a disturbed night following notice of a new lockdown in your part of the world and as you tossed and turned you thought that might be of our topic of conversation. Well, and this by now will not surprise you, they are both aspects of the same question and that is about the universality of the mind and the Vale of Thought, am I right?'

Dorothy: *Smiling to herself.* 'Yes you are right. What followed from those thoughts were my anxiety that if I, we, are too concrete in our discussions then in years to come I might look back and feel foolish about what I wrote and believed at that time.'

Librarian: 'Is that because your knowledge, or mine, will have expanded?'

Dorothy: 'Yes, I suppose so.'

Librarian: 'Then I jolly well hope you're right! I hope in years to come our knowledge is greater than it is now and not just ours but mankind's too. There is no finality in needing to learn dear one, look behind me and around at the infinite number of books, all recording lives, experience, experiments, professorships, scientific discoveries and doctors of learning. Then look up far beyond your vision to where the Masters and Elohim are learning to, creating still, making adjustments here and there as the consequences of freewill manifest in Spirit. How could knowledge ever be static, and indeed would you want it to be?

'Thirty years ago you read the Teachings that became the mainstay of your knowledge and vocabulary, you returned to them over and again, sometimes in great detail, and each time you found something new. Now was that because words had been added in the interim? Of course not, it is because people learn at their own pace and are attracted to what is immediately relevant, later that very same document might evoke a different response.

'Indeed, a spiritual Teaching should always evoke a different response because the matrix of inner learning that it is illuminating grows over time, so the sparks of knowledge have further to travel and more connections to complete.

'How have our conversations affected you may I ask?'

Dorothy: 'Each time we speak, I feel moved and surprised at what has come forth. There is a definite moment when I feel that I should stop, which is often tinged with sadness, as if I am walking from one world into another. There is a tiny struggle, as if my mind wants to continue the exploration, but my emotional self needs time to absorb the information.'

Librarian: 'And that is accurate because you are on earth to live life to the full, communing with the Spirit world and allowing it to guide you, but not allowing it to take over. Your ability to move between worlds, as you put it, has come from years of development. In previous reflections you have discussed having delusions, one of the central lessons for mankind is overcoming the delusion that he, or she, is mightier than God. The belief that if they want something to happen, then it must be right.

'It takes learning, discipline and missteps before freewill can be harnessed in service of the soul and even then it is a mutable connection throughout all of the life on earth. It is your experience of delusion that makes you cautious now, and it is always important to be careful when surrendering to inspiration for not all inspiration is Love-based.'

Dorothy: 'Is there a means of protection then?'

Librarian: 'It is the process that is second nature to you, first you say prayers and you imbibe the Christos Light, which is the Love aspect of God, and then you open to inspiration. You have been guided well over the years, and the Light you have absorbed provides a degree of protection for you and those you work with. However, each morning you renew that connection before, as you put it, moving between the worlds. Not that any physical movement takes place, of course, it is a shift in vibration and thought.

'Which brings us neatly to your question of the day I believe?'

Dorothy: 'Yes it does.'

Librarian: 'You were musing on the power of thought which we discussed yesterday, a tricky subject for you, I know, as it is inextricably linked with your mother's accusations that your "thoughts are real".

'You were trying to imagine the scope and power of the Universal Mind at the heart of Creation, as well as pondering on how mankind would normally dismiss the idea that the mind and brain are separate. You were thinking of all the times when simple occurrences would indicate a universal field of thought; a friend calling when you have just thought of them; the number of similar inventions all happening together. Or the swathes of concern and outrage that encircle your earth quicker than any computer signal. Even your restless night — possibly — affected by the collective anxieties of those facing the lockdown or scared of the virus itself.

'You have created in your mind's eye a location, you might say, where you and I commune. A vast library greater than even your imagination can comprehend, containing and cataloging all the experiences of all the lives of mankind. You could have ascribed a single physical persona to me, but you did not, because although there is something recognisable about me and our dialogue is intimate, it is also broader than a cosy one-to-one chat. Therefore, on balance, you consider me to be more of a conductor in an orchestra than a single instrument and you are right in many ways.

'You recognise that your imagery is personal and indicative of your background and yet, it may surprise you to learn, what you have imagined exists in Spirit and will continue to exist for as long as you and I commune. You have a safe space in which I am always present and when you "leave" I feel the shift, but my attention, like yours, is not singular and I to play many parts.'

Dorothy: 'That has brought tears to my eyes, for I saw it just as a fantastical explanation that describes an impression.'

Librarian: 'It exists because it contains elements of Truth that are important for mankind. Firstly, there is the sense of an archive, that what has gone before is not just recorded in fossils and landscapes, but in energy too. All experience is tangible and valuable to the Spirit world and to the souls that have either incarnated, are incarnate, or wish to be.

'Your vast corridors of knowledge represent the Light Streams down which each soul travels and to which they bring back their experience. It is important for mankind to recognise that every person on earth has a purpose and that although that purpose is individual, it is also part of a collective stream of knowledge that is essential for all.

'You imagine the corridors in your library infused with colour; blue for intellectual knowledge, purple for spiritual development, gold for teaching, pink for healing ... Then imagine those colours merging and blending as the knowledge is shared before being ultimately absorbed by the Masters and Teachers of Light, who seek to bring wisdom to mankind in ways that are current and acceptable to them.

'And I, your Librarian, representing your Higher Self. That great coordinator, mindful of all its charges, at the same time as engaging in the activities and development of all souls, in all the Realms in Spirit and on Earth. A mind that can scour the myriad corridors searching for a soul in need and bring them succour, or bring them into the Light so they can share their life and new-found understanding with a visitor, such as yourself.'

Dorothy: *Sighs*. 'So what you have said, beautifully I might say, is that my mother was right!'

Librarian: 'Truths used as weapons are the most deadly weapons of all. For all Truth contains Love and when delivered without that Love it will close hearts faster than any bullet and has the same potential to be fatal to the understanding of the recipient.'

Tiredness & powerlessness

Dorothy: 'I am sitting here seeing crystal clear pink Light, feeling peaceful and wondering if our collaboration is fading?'

Librarian: 'Why would you think that, do you think I might run out of topics?'

Dorothy: 'I don't know really, I just feel uncertain and perhaps a little tired.'

Librarian: 'Then let me speak to that, to the tiredness that is affecting you and humanity as a whole. The tiredness you are experiencing arises from a deep source within the earth itself. Whilst spiritually minded people speak about the destruction of the earth, the pollution, and the devastation, what is rarely, if ever, acknowledged is the amount of human energy that all this consumption and commerce takes up. When you add to this the last few months, now stretching into the future, the effect of the virus, the widespread grief and fear — all of this is exhausting at an emotional level as well as at a physical one.

'People are always connecting to some device or another or to the internet and appear to have more knowledge about the wider world than ever before, but what are they connecting to? Is it their soul, their inner guidance? Is meditation now one App among many rather than an intimate process, an inner calling to calm?'

Dorothy: 'I have to stop here I am not sure whose voice I am capturing, it sounds like something I might say.

Long pause ... 'OK, I am back to some sense of calm, I am seeing a soft pink and gold and hearing the word "persevere", but I am feeling a sense of exhaustion that I was unaware of earlier today.'

Librarian: 'That is because modern life is exhausting and at its heart it is consuming the consumers themselves. It is manipulating their freewill, encouraging dependency, and it is covering the fertile ground of this world with factories, warehouses, and offices whilst housing people away from the very ground they need to feed their families.

'When you remove people from the earth you disconnect them from the seasons, from the natural rhythms of life, from their appreciation of what it is to be human, vulnerable to poor harvests and the spread of disease. They become selfish, not consciously so, or intentionally, or through malevolence, but because their roots have been pruned by the generation before them and the one before that.

'This is what the virus is exposing and part of the grief that is so abundant, but unacknowledged, is a growing sense of helplessness. You have expressed it yourself, but that feeling of powerlessness is endemic and like hamsters on a wheel everyone fears that if they stop running the consequences might be too much to bear. Those consequences are not just financial, or practical, but emotional too, as the weight of regret can weigh heavily on the shoulders of generations.

'The amount of energy being utilised in a form of collective denial would power food production in a village for a year if you harnessed that energy towards the common good. But, this is not the time for righteous anger, it is a call to compassion because the failings have been fuelled by ignorance. Berating people for their shortcomings does little to open them up to the Light or to their soul guidance.

'The progenitors of real change will be those whose roots remain firmly planted in the soil of the earth that they love with every cell of their being and in the Spirit realms where their souls and Higher selves have made an unbreakable covenant with God. These beautiful Bearers of Light do not carry the legacy of greed. They come with clear eyes and fresh minds to release man from prison, freeing humanity to be who they truly are, and to know who they are, children of God and bearers of the Christos Light.'

Dorothy: 'Thank you for continuing this morning, as I was feeling so reluctant and hesitant at one point. I know as the days pass I am going to be increasingly expecting it to end, as all good things must come to an end. I fear that, for everyday I sense that our dialogue comes to a natural end and I feel complete at that point.'

Librarian: 'That is good, and I know this morning we took a direction that perhaps surprised you, for even reluctance and apprehension have their place in a spiritual dialogue. I am expecting you to apply some discrimination to what I offer for this, I hope, is an ongoing dialogue and there is always time for refinement and clarification later. But if we are both anxious from day one of getting every word-perfect then we are both setting ourselves up to fail. Can you accept your sense of completion as good a guide as any to a successful morning?'

Dorothy: 'Yes I think so ... but immediately I think that even setting up an expectation of a daily conversation is too much. The last thing I would ever want to do is to make things up to fulfil an unreasonable expectation.'

Librarian: 'I would remind you of our earlier discussions about how your own personal history affects the way you see the world. Your anxiety about endings does, of course, come from your early experience of your father leaving and growing up in circumstances where money was tight. You learnt not to expect much and have a tendency to see others as more worthy than yourself. This is an error of thinking in spiritual terms because the Love that is offered is infinite, our conversations are symbols of a relationship that is eternal and so however much you capture is entirely up to you.

'If you start to believe you have had enough and that you have no right to expect any more from me, then your expectations are not too high, but too low. Too low of me who has a great deal to offer to you and to the world in which you live, a world, may I say that is starving with harvests filled with chaff.

'I am not speaking though you to amuse or entertain, but to bring a sense of peace and a new perspective to old familiar problems and to the urgent challenges that humanity seem intent on ignoring. Challenges, which may I say, humanity is not only well-placed to resolve, but are the only means of resolution. Resolutions that will only be achieved through the application of Love and with the assistance of spiritual Light.

'The first step, the very first step, is for mankind to turn their face towards God and allow that sense of completeness into their hearts too. For once they are complete they, and this planet, can start to heal and fulfil its purpose.

'Until tomorrow Dorothy.'

The energy of thought

People talk of separation,
and much fear is generated,
because the energy of thought
is really underrated.

The weightlessness of thought
is a beauty to behold.
It is the colour stream of life
that your closed lids can enfold.

You will find within your palette
all the pastels and the jewels,
those colours merge with Spirit
and enhance those molecules.

Then within the deeper colours
are your earthy, denser shades,
the heavier thoughts of life
that no one can evade.

Your soul provides the pigments
for your purpose to succeed,
how you choose to wield your brush
is up to you indeed.

Each brush stroke that you make,
leaves an imprint on the mind,
a tracery of Light
that exists beyond all time.

Conscious cooperation

Librarian: 'Shalom to you this morning, a morning in which you have had to overcome both internal and external obstacles and yet here you are, responding to what you considered my final words of yesterday to be, a challenge.

'Now, what do you think I might have been challenging yesterday, if I was indeed challenging you?'

Dorothy: 'My reluctance and hesitancy I suppose to really believe what I am writing is not made up by me, or the result of some ambition or expectation.'

Librarian: 'We would not be speaking, or you would not be having this internal debate, if there was not some imperative within you that is other worldly, shall we say. I would be interested to hear your thoughts on how a soul might influence a personality in life, a personality that after all houses it and is the only physical means by which it can fulfil its purpose.'

Dorothy: 'My understanding is that it is through the person's conscience.'

Librarian: 'That is correct, but that tends to imply that the soul's influence is most keenly felt when the personality has erred or is troubled in some way, when some need, or regret, activates their conscience. But what of the quiet times in life when the personality is not exactly reaching out, or up, but coasting along?

'Although the Soul lives in a timeless Realm, the finite nature of life is apparent to them. So, they might see age approaching, or opportunities fading, and know that if their personality does not act, they will regret it later, what then? Would conscience alone be enough to evoke a response, and how would you square a reluctant participant with the sacrosanct nature of freewill?'

Dorothy: 'What I realised as you are speaking is how attached I am to remaining in and of the world and yet how I love exploring something greater. Something I don't fully understand, which has an element of mystery, uncertainty, and surprise within it, but is trustworthy and a balm in life, but still not something I wish to surrender to entirely.'

Librarian: 'That is important, for no spiritual Teacher would expect total surrender, not only because freewill is sacrosanct, but because your path is individual. Certainly, no personality on the earth could ever know the purpose of your soul's journey, except in the broadest terms.

'Even Masters of Light, who have access to your soul and Higher Self, do not seek surrender, they work through conscious cooperation and the voluntary setting aside of freewill in favour of the greater purpose. There is no setting aside of personal responsibility within a spiritual discipline and an unwilling, or resentful, disciple is no disciple at all.'

Dorothy: 'So, what I am taking from this is that there will always be uncertainty. Whist in life I am always going to be standing on the threshold. So, all I can do is learn to trust myself, accept that I am going to constantly be making fine assessments and that I will get it wrong sometimes too.'

Librarian: 'That's about it and I am tempted to say at this point, "get over it". But that would be harsh, because those fine assessments are just that, gossamer fine. Like spider's silk they are so strong they weave a tapestry in your soul of your journey through life, a tapestry that will last for eternity.

'Never give up your self-reflection and questioning. You are exactly where you need to be; neither completely of the earth nor of Spirit, but moving between the two and taking the Light of Spirit to the darkness of the earth, Light beam by Light beam. When your tapestry of life is complete, those strands of Light will shimmer with intelligence and help other souls who are preparing to incarnate.

'Meanwhile you have these dialogues and this writing and as the words fall they are lit and if you represent them faithfully, as you do, those Light beams will persist and awaken the hearts of any reader.'

Petals & spirals

Librarian: 'Shalom to you this morning and before you speak, can I ask you to close your eyes again and remember what you have just seen?'

Dorothy: 'It was so fleeting I'm hardly certain. The best way I can describe it is a shower of small cups, rose petal shapes, in a soft translucent blue with tiny golden spirals nestled in them floating around me. They've gone now.'

Librarian: 'Do you have any explanation?'

Dorothy: 'No, except there is a sense of something settling around me, like a shawl that wraps around the top half of my body, it's very steadying, peaceful and the colour makes it feel like a placid pool.'

Librarian: 'That is good, that is not an explanation but an experience and it means you are reaching out with your emotional body first and establishing, almost literally, the ground for inspiration. Now, naturally, you breathe into that space and metaphorically move towards the threshold that we spoke of yesterday.

'It is all a matter of vibration not movement, but the image of the placid pool indicates an empty mind, free of expectations and ready to follow, not lead.

'So walk with me a while. Allow that pool to be bathed in moonlight, see the moon reflected within it and feel the cool air around you as you realise you are sitting by the pool at night. You are alone sitting in a bench by the reeds that frame the pool and which are moving very gently in the breeze. You pull your shawl around your shoulders and look up at the stars.

'The night is clear, you are at peace. Suddenly, you feel someone sit down gently on the bench beside you, you are not alarmed because you had anticipated their arrival. You keep your eyes closed because you sense that this presence is joining with you in the silence and the two of you sit side by side in quiet contemplation, eyes closed, for quite a few moments. It is blissful.

''You both open your eyes at the same time and nod and smile to each other. You are looking at a beautiful young man, ethereal in form so everything is indistinct, but you imagine a soft robe that is pearlescent and his feet, naked and beautiful with long toes. He has a soft beard, hair to his shoulders and his hands gently folded in his lap.

'Neither of you speak, you continue to watch the pool and the moonlight and notice that he sits very still indeed until he reaches over and gently takes your hand. You offer no resistance as he opens your fingers and draws on your palm a spiral and then indicates that you should place your two palms together, which you do.

'You close your eyes to feel the effect of the spiral and the clasping of your palms, and you feel a gentle warmth moving between them and though your heart. You look up to thank the young man, but he is no longer there, his departure was a silent as his arrival and you feel touched by the encounter and moved by it. It is as if he has awoken your palms to the peace within.'

Dorothy: 'That was beautiful, thank you.'

Librarian: 'This was not just imagery Dorothy it was an experience of the peace within moving without, through your palm chakras, and into the world. It was a visualisation designed to enable you, through your own thought processes, to activate the crystals in your palm chakras to vibrate with the inner peace that you were, and are, feeling.

'The image of a Christ-like figure is a representation of the Christos which, when harnessed through the mind in this way, can positively activate healing energy. It was gentle, soundless and something which once felt will never be forgotten, for it is simple and its potential is only limited by your imagination. That energy just flows into the world and it matters not whether you direct it or not because it is greater than you, but it cannot benefit the world without you and others like you.

'Each morning you discuss the virulence of the virus and its apparent ability to transmit itself silently and invisibly throughout all the populations of your world. That is nothing, nothing. I tell you, to the power of people who turn their minds to transmitting Love to their world and bringing healing swiftly and silently to their brothers and sisters in the Light. No living being could vaccinate themselves against that for Love is life itself.'

Courage & confidence

Dorothy: 'Shalom and good morning. I have just deleted my last entry because I doubted the consistency of the flow of Light within the words, but its deletion has made me sad. It is important for me to recapture my gratitude for the imagery of the pale blue rose petals and the fragile spirals, like tiny palms reaching down and planting the seed of life. The colour of the petals was the colour of water, so essential to life, so it summed up Creation in such a beautiful way and made me feel grateful for my life.'

Librarian: 'We feel your sadness too. We see the plans, the care, the Love and the potential being so carefully planted and watch helplessly as the harvest fails through lack of nurture or fear. We do not have a body, but we have hearts and emotional bodies that merge with those we work with in life, and with the natural world, so we feel its pain as acutely as you feel a pain in your knee.

'Earlier this morning in meditation where you were sitting overlooking a peaceful lake, reflecting the valley around it and the sky above it. You merged with the landscape and for that moment you were formless. You became aware that the wooden platform you were sitting on was still connected to the trees from which it was hewn. That is how we see life on earth, we see and respond to the natural world as if we are part of it because we are. The vibration of the trees in a forest is as much a part of my world as the wind through them is part of yours. There is no separation, we are all part of Creation and affected by it and able to affect it.

'So the visualisation of the rose petals affected you because you saw the Truth within it, and I know it also provoked a sense of regret for past failings and a bout of self recrimination, which is no longer helpful. That is why you were urged to delete that entry earlier, not because it did not flow, but because it took you to a place you no longer need to go. You are talking to me now, you have found your way here and I am not going to allow this opportunity to pass. Yes, the road here has been rocky and you have acted in ways you now regret. Your eyes have been opened to the tragic loss of opportunity and the dried up harvest. But you have been forgiven and have gone as far as any human being can go in forgiving others, for this was not a singular failing. Now, just as you wiped the page clean this morning it is time to wipe the past clean and to open your eyes to the spirals of potential already nestling in your heart and mine. I always knew you were coming, I did not know how long it would take you to arrive, but your arrival and this communication is as important to me as it is to you. Are you ready?

'Every day you say you believe in the Light, so this is your challenge, is it not? Are you actually willing to consider that, while you are on earth, the Light that has been released through your trials and tribulations is now waiting to lead you forward? That nothing more can be gained through regret and sadness and that continuing to fuel these emotions restricts your ability, and now mine, to move forward in the world and bring our combined Light to bear?

'Now, I mean no judgement of you here, but consider for one moment how comfortable and familiar that cloak of regret and sadness has become. How easy it would be to nestle under it until your time in earth is complete and then to make peace in your soul body. How little you would have to risk, how safe your life would be because you have enough people around you who would sympathise with your backstory and who would see that as the reason for you not to thrive. In fact, it would even suit their analysis at the time of you as a victim. But do you expect yourself not to thrive?'

Dorothy: 'That's true. Hard to say and admit to myself, but yes, I have accepted that my aspirations in life have been curtailed, even shown up to be ridiculous.'

Librarian: 'And yet, you still found your way here and I still waited. Do you really feel that someone like myself would continue to trust in a Light that had failed? Look around you at the number of charges I have, at the complexity of my domain, at your ability to engage with me without fear or shielding your eyes. I know you Dorothy and I know your soul and even beyond that. If I can put my trust in you why can't you trust yourself?

'You are greatly loved beloved one and not just by me. You have our respect, but self-respect cannot be imposed even by a Master of Light, that tiny flame within that you have cowled needs to be uncovered and allowed to breathe the oxygen that is plentiful around it. No one is asking you to proclaim anything, take on the world or prove any points, just to allow that fragile, gentle spiral that is Dorothy to fulfil its purpose and in so doing help others in Spirit fulfil theirs.'

Dorothy: 'Every morning when we talk you surprise me and today is no exception, I hear what you're saying I really do and for much of my life I considered myself courageous, but that did come to an end.'

Librarian: 'If it had truly come to an end we would not be speaking, this is the most courageous thing you will ever be faced with Dorothy, release your Light from its cowl and let our work together truly begin.'

An inner journey of faith

Dorothy: 'Shalom, I want to come here today and say, "yes, you're right, I'm happy to move on and celebrate whatever comes", but I still experience reluctance and fear, with a small "f".'

Librarian: 'No one can lift fear from you and neither should they, fear has a purpose which is to prevent harm. But what purpose do you think it plays when the prospect of harm comes from within the person themselves?'

Dorothy: 'Slowing them down, making them think before acting impulsively?'

Librarian: 'In other words it creates a little space, some thinking time, and what is wrong with that?'

Dorothy: 'Nothing I guess unless that turns into stasis and missed opportunities.'

Librarian: 'And you have enough examples around you to know how that plays out, but equally impulsive actions have led to missed opportunities because of their negative consequences, so there is a balance to be struck in life.

'In Spirit, without the pressure of time, the value we place on space is different, the easiest analogy I can think of is sitting on a shore watching and waiting for the fishing boats to arrive. You know they are expected because the community needs food, and yet the weather and the tides are not conducive to their safe passage.

'So you choose the elder fisherman of the village to be an outlook, his eyes may not be the best but his understanding of the tides and of the currents is second to none. He feels the weather in his bones, and he can follow the stars with his eyes closed. So, you do not find him sitting on an outcrop of rock with a telescope clamped to his eye. You find him standing with the wind moving through him, his eyes closed, every fibre in his body alert to the sea, the tides, and the pull of the moon. He has infinite patience and waits to guide that vessel home with his heart and his mind, for he loves those on board and rides every wave with them.'

Dorothy: 'So the space that is needed is not just an external lack of activity, but not filling the inner space with chatter?'

Librarian: 'Absolutely, it is one thing to ask a human being to let go of past events and the feelings that have accrued, it is quite another to move from years of chatter into silence. But, like the fisherman on that rock it, takes time to discover that that silence is not silent at all, it is filled with the movements of the tides, the moon, the Spheres, and humanity.

'It is a case of tuning into the language of Light, of learning to recognise the shifts and the needs of both Spirit and mankind. For when those two align it creates a portal through which Spirit and mankind can send Light into an area of darkness, or need, that has a practical application which Spirit alone cannot produce.

'It is not automatic, it takes a long time to learn and a degree of discipline to clear out the chatter of life and to sense and interpret those subtleties. It requires, and teaches, patience but its companion is peace and its gift a sense of belonging, not to the world alone but to Creation.

'Is this a journey you are willing to take? A journey you will not complete in this lifetime and which you can but glimpse while on earth. A journey that takes you away from the maelstrom of the ocean of life and into the quiet reflective pools where no accolades exist, no recognition, no proof, just faith and belief?

'Look behind me Dorothy at your imagined world of past lives stored one upon another, stretching back into infinity. Imagine the learning that has accrued, the number of incarnations mankind has gone through, the number of past lives your soul has lived, and yet mankind is on the brink of disaster like never before.

'Think of all the prophets, the Teachers, the naysayers. Of the scrolls of papyrus and reams of paper filled with spiritual teachings, of the Holy Books, what do they all have in common; an exhortation to believe in the Light. The Light of the Prophets, the Light of God, the Light of the Christ ... and yet so little is spoken of the Light within, the God within. That still small voice that can sense the movement of the Spheres, the pain within humanity and can respond instantaneously without ceremony or cost.

'That is the journey you are being invited to make, and that is why the space is clearing around you and within you. This is an inner journey of faith for the flame that ignites those candles is the Light of the Christos and that nestles in every petal that comes to this earth.'

The work begins

Librarian: 'Shalom to you this day and peace be with you and around you, as it is at this moment.'

Dorothy: 'Shalom, thank you. I do feel peaceful and it settled on me, along with an image, during our earlier meditation.'

Librarian: 'What did you see?'

Dorothy: 'It was more of sensing the Library and taking a seat within it rather than standing. I had the feeling of settling into a comfortable armchair with a table to one side and candlelight illuminating the shelves all around. I was completely at home and you were seated too, although I had the feeling that sometimes I could be alone here.

'You were appeared different today, still bearded and with shoulder-length hair, but less stereotypical of the sculptures of ancient prophets. You are quiet and gentle, moving slowly and deliberately, and when the candlelight catches your hair there is an auburn and gold hue that I see. You have beautiful hands with long fingers and bright blue eyes that smile and encourage. I get the sense that you love to talk, to share and to communicate and that you are very interested in any visitor to the library and go out of your way to making them feel at home.'

Librarian: 'Well it seems it is my turn to be flattered for you see me very well today. I have often imagined how I might have looked on the earth and, of course, I am very familiar with all the Etheric bodies that cloak the souls when they first return. I love to see the flowing beards, the wild hair and the wild eyes and wonder how mankind at that time would have reacted to a prophet who looked like that. I imagined him, for it was always a him, strolling off in front of a line of people expecting them to follow, or bellowing from some hilltop and putting the fear of God into them.

'But my role is, and always has been, different, you see me as a Librarian someone who manages and catalogues all the lives of all the souls that have incarnated. One who, for want of a better word, is a housekeeper of souls, and you are right in part. But I also soothe, explain and nurture and so for me to appear with wild hair and wild eyes would not be helpful, even though it might well be what some returning souls would expect to find, as you did.

'Although those images are rife throughout your religions and places of worship, it is a misinterpretation of what a homecoming really means. Homecoming is reuniting with those that have gone before and an opening to the true learning available throughout the Spirit realms.

'There is no external judgement, no St. Peter waiting at the gate, but there is the reflection of the soul and the acknowledgement of the Truth within the life just spent in conversation with the Higher Self. Some of those realisations can be painful, and the soul needs time and support to integrate the learning and accept any karma that has accrued.

'So, it is important that a central figure like myself is neutral, shall we say, able to soothe and nurture where needed. However, to complete your vision of a library, someone who ensures that the returning souls find their way home and that their experience is shared. Even if they see me as a stereotypical wild prophet at first the softer image will always take precedence eventually. Remember, there is no distinction between male and female in Spirit, so I am always recreated in the image that best suits their need for comfort.

'Now to return to your imagery of us sitting together, what did you make of that?'

Dorothy: 'Well it felt significant, settling, it seems to signify my feeling of comfort at being here, a familiarity and a sense of knowing that I was welcome. I could just sit and be present, or we could sit and talk as friends, although that feels presumptuous after so short a time. I saw books piled up on the table beside me, not giving details of individual lives, but of patterns and examples.'

Librarian: 'You are right and it is not presumptuous at all for I have known you since before you were born and you have known me. The sense of friendship you feel is, in fact, shared purpose, because there is a tremendous, unrecognised need in humanity at this time to move back from the brink. It is visible to them through the pollution of their seas and rivers, the loss of species', the drying up of resources, the enduring inequality and poverty across the globe and the outbreaks of war, violence, pestilence, and disease. But the remedy, if that's what it is, is not so visible as the churches and the religious organisations are not meeting the needs of many and are fuelling division in some.

'Humanity needs to see and feel the same Light that you do when you come here, and to allow themselves to become curious about their soul purpose. To understand that humanity is one organism and that by embracing diversity and working together they can heal their world, heal each other and thrive. To achieve this, they need to discover and follow the lanterns that are already lit along the paths that lead to success and salvation.

'You are right to see yourself seated as significant, two days ago, I asked if you were ready to remove your Light from its cowl and begin our work together? The fact that you see yourself seated and settled is my answer. You are no longer standing ready to take off, or arguing with yourself about the importance of these meditations, you are settling back and ready to see what comes.

'You saw piles of books on the table beside you stretching high above you. I know you saw no details of those lives just the sheer number of incarnations that could be distilled into one — often thwarted — lesson, that of learning patience.'

Dorothy: 'That's right I did. I thought that for many people past lives are only significant if they've been kings or queens or prophets. However, if a library like this were to exist, you would find stacks of lives of ordinary people; bus drivers, beggars, priests, doctors, actors, farmers, prisoners ... all needing to learn the same lesson: patience.'

Librarian: 'Absolutely, for it is the simple things in life that can be the most important and the merest slight in life that can create the most intractable karma that can feed conflict down the generations. Patience, tolerance, love, and peace are core lessons, whether you are a king or a pauper, and yet they are the hardest to learn. That pile of books on your table could topple and fall a hundred feet, and even then only represent a tiny percentage of people from all walks of life who have failed to learn those lessons. Who transferred their anger and frustration onto others, even ending lives in the process, rather than accept the lesson and move on.

'So you are welcome to sit with me and in this place anytime. It may surprise you, this is the work, our work, to follow the patterns in the lines of Light that weave through this place. To find ways to bring that understanding to life so that humanity can begin to visualise their power and potential for good and for healing.

'Spirit cannot do that alone, there have to be bridges, and conduits of Light. There are the Bearers of Light, but they too need help and support and those already established in life who can hold up a lantern for them too.'

The wishing well

Come stand by this well and what do you see,
a glassy surface, a mirror maybe?
Your face there reflected, more lined than before,
your sadness compacted, for your heart is still sore.

But let me remind you of one thing you know,
a phrase you use often, 'as above, so below.'
And then in this image what do we see?
A collection of wishes that were not meant to be.

But then we look upwards, to the light on your face,
to your heartfelt commitment, your increasing grace.
And the treasure this well was built to contain
is reflected back softly, no longer arcane.

For out of the darkness this Light's been released,
the millennium saw its power much increased.
This promise not hidden in dank wishing wells,
lives on in all hearts wherein it does dwell.

The library reimagined

Librarian: 'Shalom to you this day and I am aware that this will be an unusual contact for you have visited in your dream state and have, I believe, some things you wish to share first.'

Dorothy: 'Yes, that's right but first shalom and thank you. I do, however, have difficulty in writing what I imagined and I find that incredible because after all it is my imagination, yet still. it is hard to capture and describe.

'I found myself dreaming of being in the Library alone and being allowed, even invited, to explore. I was aware that I was floor-bound, so to speak, and so much of the activity was happening way above me. At first, the passageways appeared ancient, narrow, and similar to the streets of London before the great fire. There were families and activities happening behind the facades high above me. Souls, I assume, were coming and going, families meeting in huge groups, hospitals, bakeries, churches, all aspects of city life at that time.

'Then I saw the gardens, many gardens all of different designs, courtyard, Japanese, Middle Eastern, Indian and single people sitting in the shade or by water fountains, or beside oasis' in the desert deep in thought and reflection.

'As I woke up, the imagery became more modern and akin to the banks of television screens that we see in theatres where we have virtual audiences, but without the framework of the technology. Of course, these screens would be much higher and more international like the advertising screens in a city centre, but mute, delicate and lit naturally not artificially.'

Librarian: 'And what did you see behind those screens?'

Dorothy: 'As I turn my attention to the speck that represents the spine of the books, I see represented there all aspects of life and culture, every country and Age. It is as if the stories are all taking place behind the spine.'

Librarian: 'Well, you already know that souls, once they return, carry with them their etheric body which is an energetic copy, shall we say, of their physical form. It has no skeleton to keep it upright and so learning how to move with this jelly-like structure can take time, and cause some amusement. In the early days, weeks, months, or years of being in Spirit there is a form which creates for itself a familiar environment which serves as a transitional base.

'How long those forms last depends on the spiritual awareness of the homecoming soul. Because the environment they create needs to be familiar to them, it is as diverse as your world is now and as it has been since its inception. Homecoming souls tend to recreate gardens or natural environments, especially those that need time to recuperate. And, yes, I can quite see how even imagining such complexity, all working in harmony and with purpose can be hard indeed.'

Dorothy: 'Is the Etheric body eventually shed?'

Librarian: 'Yes, that's right, often when another aspect of that Soul has incarnated and that can be any length of earth time at all.'

Dorothy: 'So does that form stay available, shall we say, so that the soul can enrobe themselves in it to greet a homecoming soul, to make themselves recognisable?'

Librarian: 'Yes indeed and rather like our conversations it is a combination of two things, the thought process of the resident soul and what they desire to project and the expectation of the homecoming soul. They may recognise something familiar, the inflection in the voice for example, and then imagine the shape of the speaker. When those two factors meet, expectation and mind pictures, then the Etheric representation is strong.'

'Well I liked your imagery, which, as you know, can only ever conjure up your life experience with perhaps some added sensations from your past lives in Spirit bringing a little sparkle and mystery. What is important is that it has changed the impression you have created of an old dusty library where you might find history stored in neat rows. Instead, you find a dynamic World, or Worlds, where life, learning, and Love continues undaunted by the loss of a human form, and perhaps even more vibrant because of the harmony and sense of purpose that pervades all things. I hope we talk again later.'

...

Librarian: 'Welcome back and you are right in thinking that I would like to continue to explore your imagery and expound upon it. But first may I say how delighted I am to have these opportunities and how grateful, for you are helping me achieve my purpose as I am helping you and that is joyous is it not? At this time on Earth when there is so much uncertainty, pain, and grief you have found your way to a place where the lack of stasis is a constant. Where change is welcome because it signifies movement and learning, and movement and learning are the pathways to the ultimate, which is to merge with the God energy. That is the ultimate for all Higher Selves.

'So within your imagery you had rows, or levels, of activity and that to my way of thinking represents the hierarchy within the Spirit realms, or the progression, towards finer and finer vibrations all achieved through learning and acceptance. You saw constant movement between all the levels and I know at first you interpreted that as homecoming souls and in many ways you are right, especially at this time. But there are other channels of movement too, shall we say, as souls from different levels commune together, visit Teachers or Masters for example for some instruction, or even attend magnificent concerts or the Halls of Learning.

'The Spirit world is not, and I know you know this, filled with souls all moving about and bumping into one another like on your busy city streets. Spirit is more like viewing the circuitry of the brain through one of your sensitive machines. The movement you imagined was the firing of thought particles, which create the connections between souls and between Realms.

'Remember there is no time, so your vision of the ancient and modern existing side by side is accurate. The great spirals of learning affect all the Realms, they are always vibrant, for nothing is wasted as the collective Higher Selves progress towards the God energy. Nothing, to use your analogy, is allowed to gather dust in some dark corner and become outdated or irrelevant, it is all absorbed and where there has been karma created it is assuaged first.

Dorothy: 'I was also struck by the peace and harmony that I experienced.'

Librarian: 'Well yes, although that is not to say there is not some difficult soul-searching while in Spirit, The structure that you saw whether as a library, or a bank of screens, or a city, all had architectural form. It is this that represents the framework of Universal Law that all the Spirit realms operate within. Here you get to see the difference between a world committed to using and abusing freewill in every aspect — your Earth — and the Spirit realms, where the acceptance of the value and wisdom of Universal Law is universal. That acceptance evokes the peace, the sense of purpose and the progression that you witnessed.'

Dorothy: 'Then I can understand why some Masters objected to the granting of freewill because there was a beauty in the order that I saw.'

Librarian: 'That is true but you have to remember you are a visitor and, as with every tourist, you are drawn to what is new and different; the beautiful architecture, the aspirational spires and the people who catch your eye. You are less likely to explore the backstreets, or see the beggars and the poverty at first but, after taking up residence, what may have felt like a welcoming community can quickly pale when the reality sets in.

'The granting of freewill was not an idle decision, it was taken to allow deviation and challenge and to allow mankind to find their path away from the Plan as well as towards it. It enabled individuality and comparison, all within a field of Love, on a planet designed to be beautiful and to bring out the beauty in humanity and all they share their Earth with. It was a gift, a most precious gift, and it has generated profound learning which would not have been possible if it had not been granted.'

Dorothy: 'Does the content of the imagery matter?'

Librarian: 'The detail does not and I know beneath this question is another one which is, "if my imagery is so personal how could sharing it benefit anyone else and indeed could it not be misleading?'

'Well my answer is that no imagery is misleading if it develops and encourages freedom of imagination and thoughts, as yours does, for it shows the process of exploration and that is valuable. A marine scientist might have developed your images with Koi Carp that little further and extended into coral reefs where the fishes swim to certain depths, communicate one with another and you see flashes of movement and colour everywhere. An astronomer might interpret their inspirations in universes and stars, and a cook in ingredients and dishes.

'Wherever you looked whether it was in a city or at banks of screens you saw diversity, pathways of learning stretching out far beyond your vision. You were aware of healing, commerce, families, and restitution all going on throughout the Ages and that is the key; spirituality is not one path it is billions, all important. Some expressed by a shopkeeper selling food, some in governments, some in hospitals and sanctuaries and some in churches, mosques, temples, and synagogues. It matters not what interests and beliefs you follow in life, what success or failures you may suffer. What matters is the exploration itself, for the purpose of life is to find your way back home and to come to know who, or what, sent you forth.'

Dorothy: 'Thank you, once again that was beautiful.'

Releasing Light into the world

Librarian: 'I am aware of your earlier conversation about past, painful, events that have affected you and your partner very significantly and which are surfacing once again, but not as trauma, as learning. This is exactly the type of learning that homecoming souls engage with, they dredge the silt from the river, release the Light and enable the water to flow freely once more. It accounts for many of the flashes of lights and colours you saw yesterday in this place, healing observations, heartfelt acceptance and, yes, forgiveness first for the self and then others. New channels appearing all the time, more opportunities for incarnating souls, new threads of karma woven into the tapestry of Higher Selves.

'But to do it while on earth is a gift and an act of courage, for it cleanses not only yourselves, but all those involved for even if they are seemingly unaware of the shift their soul is not. As great wheels turn through time small things happen, cogs that once grated now slip easily together and the wheel that once shuddered on its axis turns silently and moves in harmony once again. Truly, it is the only time travel that is possible on Earth for it moves you through time to a new reality and a fresh start.'

Dorothy: 'That seems a lot from one conversation, one which we have had a hundred times before. I did notice it was lighter, more reflective, less combative in a way, although that seems a strange word to use in this context.'

Librarian: 'That is because there was combat on many levels because the Light was so strong in all involved. Now that may seem like a contradiction, for the Light is neither a weapon nor an adversary, it is the opposite. But it is unyielding too, for it shines as resolutely in all the rooms of the mansion that is your personality. It neither spares your blushes, nor avoids your secrets and whilst you might bask in its glow when celebrating success you can be sure it is equally bright when you wish to disappear under the covers and hide your shame.

'However, the Light of Spirit is multifaceted, it holds within it Love and peace and within those elements rest hope and joy, compassion and patience and so much more. So, as much as life's lessons are primarily tolerance, patience, and compassion, the Light of Spirit unerringly models and offers these attributes until you can absorb them into your being. It is not personal, it is the creative action of Spirit in life and it is available to all.'

Dorothy: 'I fear that this is a circular conversation because are we not then back to why humanity seems to suffer so much by turning away from the very Source of their healing?'

Librarian: 'This will always be a circular conversation Dorothy because there will never be one moment in life where all the wheels have turned in unison to release an imagined golden coin of enlightenment. Remember the architecture of the Spirit world, the levels of understanding and development, as you achieve one level you reveal the next one and so it goes for Masters, Teachers and homecoming souls alike. The Higher Selves will not be absorbed into the God energy one by one, or even two by two like Noah's Ark, all the Higher Selves will be absorbed together.'

Dorothy: 'So are you saying that at the point humanity achieves enlightenment, then "poof" we all are absorbed in one great flash of Light?'

Librarian: *Laughs.*

Dorothy: 'There is a real shift in energy as his laugh rippled through the 'bookshelves' as if all the souls suddenly pause and wait to hear his answer. There is a long pause.

Librarian: 'I believe you have a saying in your world, "that is clearly above my pay grade," and that is certainly my answer here dear one. Clearly, even after all these earth years I have not already gone "poof," as you put it, or we would not be speaking, so I cannot possibly know what the ultimate will be, or what it will feel like.

'If you were to ask me to speculate, I would be inclined to believe that there would be yet more to uncover and discover in other worlds and other universes. That mankind might yet have an existence without the burden of bodies, an existence perhaps more of the mind than the flesh.

'As I see it so much of the destruction of the planet has been driven by desires and greed. I could envisage an existence, or maybe millions of existences, where harmony, thought alone and cooperation with planetary life could create new Spheres of learning. But I don't know, or if I will ever know if the ultimate is to go "poof" in a second Big Bang. But I do know this the learning that has been absorbed through experience will never be lost. So, if there is another life after the "poof" it will benefit from all that has gone before and that is quite a thought is it not given the complexity of life experience?'

Dorothy: *He laughs again and I sit in the silence for a while aware that there is less movement than before. I still have a slight feeling of being overheard, but it is not unpleasant.*

Librarian: 'You seem quiet, have I troubled you?'

Dorothy: 'Not at all, I was just thinking of the multitudes of lives all being lived, suffered, ended prematurely, struggled though, all with the same purpose — to find and experience Love — and yet apparently so different. How relatively easy it is to be affronted, to cause affront or hurt, and yet, it is so much harder to respect and support another's path to the same goal if it looks or feels different from ours. Particularly, and I have said this before I know, in those very settings where the opposite should be true, where people have been drawn together for succour, support or Teaching, it just seems so perverse.'

Librarian: 'Do remember that not all lives have within them a spiritual purpose. As the Golden Age progresses spirituality will become much more accepted and acceptable, so there will always be difference and that is essential to choice and comparison. God did not decree the predominance of the material in life, that was mankind. As the rivers dry up, the seas choke, the harvests fail and the shops empty, then people will begin to re-examine what they value, what the earth can support and what it cannot.

'In many ways the pandemic is focussing more minds than ever before on the value of life itself, of friendships and care for one another. It is, rather like the Light we first spoke of, shining onto the dark corners of inequality, neglect, poverty, and selfishness and requiring a change of attitude and behaviour across the world. Changes that like your conversation this morning will release Light, joy and hope into the atmosphere and affect everyone universally.'

Ribbons of peace

Come, let us speak
a little each day,
let not your routines
stand in my way.

Allow those quiet moments
to flow into rhyme,
so the Love that I have
can reach beyond time.

For the words that ascend
are like ribbons of peace,
that once you take grip
bring me into reach.

And the channel that forms
brings Light into life,
moves out from your soul,
that eternal midwife.

For the souls of mankind
are united in Love
they just need alerting
by words from above.

Words that stir souls
and settle their hearts
a gentle reminder
they're never apart.

Colour Wheels

Librarian: 'I feel your hesitancy as you take your seat here today, so shall we speak or is it enough simply to sit together for a while?'

Dorothy: 'I'm not certain ... I suspect I might be pushing things this morning because my head is full of the Colour Wheel last night and my curiosity about how that is received in Spirit. I can fantasise, but will that affect our conversation?'

Librarian: 'What would your fantasies be?'

Dorothy: 'That there is a shower of colour and Light that becomes available to the Spirit realms, and because it has been touched by mankind it is of value to the world. It can be used by those souls who work within humanity or even to the earth itself.'

Librarian: 'So you do you have an image of a platoon of Spirit beings ready equipped with butterfly nets to catch the sparks of colour and Light that shower from the spiral that your wheel creates? Do you imagine them waiting in a huge circle wondering how they will know when your clocks chime seven?'

Dorothy: 'Not quite. I see it like an infinity symbol, a flow of colour directed in a continuous motion, like a stream that circles back to its Source, having first irrigated an area of need. Thinking about it, rather than the Light and colour moving out perhaps a holographic version of that need is placed into the flow, that sits better with me. I could also imagine the structure of Light as a resonance that remains after the wheel has concluded. Perhaps the energy created continues to a lesser extent between meetings, and is then reactivated when we meet again?'

Librarian: 'Interesting, there is a lot of Truth in what you describe as a fantasy. I suspect your image of the continuation of the resonance comes from your early experience of Colour Wheels. As I recall the following day you often felt not quite cohered, as if fragments of your psyche were floating around somewhere else looking for their way back home.'

Dorothy: 'You make it sound like a hangover.'

Librarian: 'Well, there is surprisingly some Truth in that too, for although during the Wheel you are grounded your consciousness is very much elsewhere and that is more akin to the dream state than it is to normal everyday living.'

'It may surprise you to know that your aura, which is the way I recognise you, carries more green within it today than yesterday, as that was the colour you represented during the Wheel. This morning that particular colour is, to use your word, resonant with meaning and purpose. It is, you might say, as if you left a little of your consciousness with the Wheel to monitor its demise, like you might watch the embers of a fire until they are fully extinguished. Although, and here you are right, a regular and reliable Colour Wheel never ceases, its Etheric remains. Even former members who have now passed to Spirit recognise its resurgence and participate from time to time.

'This is the power, the beauty, and the simplicity of thought, of collective thought, intention, and commitment. I think you would agree that a Colour Wheel requires a minimal commitment from its members and yet, its impact is so profound and needed in the world. It provides healing to those that participate and that extends to those they work with and love. It also provides Spirit with a beacon which enables them to make a palpable difference in the world.

'I think in your world war there were beacons lit across your country to warn people of oncoming danger. Now imagine that same number of beacons regularly lit up across your world signifying an inflow of peace and healing. Beautiful, timeless manifestations of Light that bring Spirit and man together in service of the whole. We talked yesterday of a 'big bang' this would not be that, but it would be a path to salvation for every living thing.

'Shalom to you this day, I am so pleased you overcame your hesitancy.'

Dorothy: 'So am I, every day this feels like a blessing and I am always surprised and grateful. Shalom to you.'

Going Greater

Librarian: 'Shalom to you this day and I am aware that you have experienced a range of emotions on your way here, shall we say?'

Dorothy: 'Shalom and yes, although I feel sad even saying it. I almost didn't visit today because I have several worldly distractions pulling at me, but as soon as I was on the verge of staying away I felt the same loss that accompanies the end of all our conversations.

'I also realised that I have mixed emotions about how to approach you. If I feel I have nothing to bring to you then I fear we will have nothing to talk about. On the other hand, if I am full of my agenda I worry that may skew yours, so those are daily anxieties that I need to overcome.'

Librarian: 'If you were to look back at our conversations, Dorothy would you say that your agenda has always had the upper hand?'

Dorothy: 'No, not at all, whatever I bring here you widen my perspective and make linkages that I would not have done.'

Librarian: 'There is another cause of your reluctance, so common that few people even attempt to overcome it, and that is the requirement that you relinquish freewill for the time that we are together. It's a strange requirement in a way, it takes your freewill to bring you to this place, then you have to "park it outside," while you are here and pick it up as you leave.

'I recall your early days as a mother when you would leave your children in their pushchair outside a shop when you went in and pick them up on leaving, is that not the case?'

Dorothy: 'That's true and it makes me wonder if the world was so different just a few years ago as no one would dare do that now, parents sweep through shops like ocean liners these days. But yes, I too saw myself leaving my baggage outside the door to enter this place ... but your description is more accurate because my children are precious and so is my freewill, so choosing to leave something precious behind in order to receive something equally precious is part of my process each day.'

Librarian: 'You speak of feeling loss each day and that means that you gain through the act of surrendering your freewill. That should tell you something should it not about how the act of surrender increases mankind's ability to ingest Light?'

Dorothy: 'Absolutely, but statements like that, although not in this context, always ring alarm bells because I feel that to let go of my discrimination is dangerous and could open me up to being manipulated by false prophets.'

Librarian: 'I would agree with you absolutely about discrimination and remind you of the sacrosanct nature of freewill. But let's explore for a minute the degrees of manipulation you already have to avoid, or may even fall prey to, every day.

'There is, I believe, a focus these days on fake news and how news organisations, governments, advertisers, scientists, religion … increasingly have the power to manipulate information and people themselves. But many of these expressions are just symptoms of how corrupted all societies have become, corrupted not only by money and greed, but by losing sight of the very reason for life itself.

'The Light of life has been cowled for too long. I asked you if you could find the courage to release your own Light. That is the same question facing all of humanity if they are to have the freedom that they need to truly thrive. I do not mean in opposition to one another but through cooperation, and by creating the psychological space where the new shoots of hope can be planted.

'How can mankind find a way forward in peace when they are shackled by their own fear to institutions that have become self-perpetuating, but not self reflective? How can humanity move forward when so few people hold the very livelihood of so many in their hands? But … and here is the conundrum … the change that is needed is first internal then external, it is towards soul and then towards the Spirit of life. It mirrors your journey here.

'Imagine if every person took that same journey each morning, finding the courage to go to what is great within themselves and consciously to bring that Light into their lives. That would be the surrender of freewill in service of the whole, a whole that would reflect Love and the Soul of humanity without the need for manipulation or coercion.'

Releasing your soul

Librarian: 'Shalom to you this day. I welcome you to this place with my love, for I so enjoy your visits.'

Dorothy: 'Shalom and I love to be here, but it seems I have to wade through sadness sometimes to make the shift, and then the doubts assail me.'

Librarian: 'I know you felt unsettled yesterday at the content of your writing. For myself I felt that you were not fully here and so I brought what I could to your worldly concerns. I had to accept that your spiritual heart had closed, but today it is open and that is where your sadness lies.'

Dorothy: 'I know, I'm sorry, yesterday I was managing my emotions from an earlier meditation and so I was defended.'

Librarian: 'Why the defences, do you not feel safe here?'

Dorothy: 'Yes, but vulnerable too, as if this is too precious to risk losing or to contemplate ever reaching a natural end, so I have to tread gently for ...'

Librarian: ' ... we are walking on your heart?'

Dorothy: 'Yes, there are no words to express how precious this is and yet, as you say, yesterday I left the most vulnerable part of myself at the doorway.'

Librarian: 'Did you really think I didn't know, that I could not have helped?'

Dorothy: 'I feel embarrassed to be indulging the misgivings that I was having out loud. Misgivings that I have nurtured for so many years and fear knowing the outcome.'

Librarian: 'I suspect that it is not knowing the outcome that you fear, but believing an outcome that is different to the script you wrote some thirty years ago is possible, is that true?'

Dorothy: 'Yes that's true, very true and so it's better not to speak of my misgivings and fears for then they might be confirmed by a Source I trust, like yourself.'

Librarian: 'Before we spoke yesterday you did share your misgivings and got a different response to the one you feared, but that did not bring you comfort, is that because you did not believe it?'

Dorothy: *Cries.* 'No, well maybe, or perhaps, after some reflection.'

Librarian: 'What would it take for you not to have certainty one way or another, but to accept that you could well have been wrong for the last thirty years? To have nothing more than an open mind?'

Dorothy: 'A belief that I am a different person to the person I was thirty years ago, a belief in the Teachings I have followed and the Teachers who channelled them.'

Librarian: 'So, are you saying that in order to be "good enough", however you might interpret that, you weren't enough as you were thirty years ago you had to change yourself to become acceptable?'

Dorothy: 'Yes, something like that, clearly given the dissent, the arguments, the shunning, there was something deeply unacceptable about me to others attracted to the same path. So, something had to change, for many of my fellow travellers that change meant they left, I didn't do that, but the personal cost was high.'

Librarian: 'Do you believe at this moment that what you call deeply unacceptable to others was, or is, deeply unacceptable to God?'

Dorothy: 'Not any more, for a few years I did.'

Librarian: 'And that is when you wrote the script for the part of this journey you're now struggling with?'

Dorothy: 'Yes.'

Librarian: 'I need you to listen to these words Dorothy and listen carefully. You are bright and intelligent, and you have absorbed more of the Teachings than many of your fellow travellers. At a deep level you understand the interconnectedness of all things, the need of the Soul to experience life and the assuaging of karma. You have felt the deep Love of Spirit and you can return it and you have seen the wisdom of your Master's play out over the years time and time again. Do you really believe after all this that they were so wrong about you?'

Dorothy: 'No, but ...'

Librarian: 'Can you accept that the learning that you undertook was driven by your soul in order that it could shine in this world? That your Masters and Teachers stood side by side with your soul while your personality battled to keep walking the path your soul had chosen. That what was unhelpful was peeled away to expose the Being of Light that you are, a Being occluded by life, but that wished to be free? A Being known and loved and nurtured by your Masters until you can nurture that Being yourself and unlock it from the prison of your own fears?

'A Being, Dorothy, that you have to accept as worthy, and as loveable in the eyes of God. How can you have compassion and belief in others if you cannot believe in yourself, in the Light at your core that is part of the Christos Light? A Light that only you can try to separate off, as you tried to yesterday, but which is as visible to Spirit as your moon is to you.'

Dorothy: 'It all seems so simple and obvious when you say it, so I'm nodding away and yes, I am listening. I realise that the answer to my "wait and see" question is in my own hands, no one else can make this shift for me.'

Librarian: 'Indeed, why do you think after thirty years of struggle you found the Light that led you down the corridor to the Library of Lives? That set up the armchair in which you could rest a while and take stock?

'Strange as this may seem, it was your ability to keep walking that removed most of your prison bars. It was your soul's decision and purpose not to turn away, like others did, but like any removal of prison bars you are removing both their protection and their confinement and both are painful.

'What you are now confronting is the remainder of the mental constructs that you still carry, unexamined and untested, and which could yet hold you back without the help of Spirit, which is there for you in abundance.'

Dorothy: 'And I accept that help and I am grateful for it, thank you, as always, much to think about.'

Librarian: 'You have to follow the sadness sometimes for that is your soul crying for release, and that is what you do. I, too, am grateful for your courage and tenacity. Until tomorrow, I hope. Shalom'.

Spiritual words

Spiritual words
are designed to impart
the truth that is Love
direct to your heart.

For the message they bring
lives far beyond time,
this poet embroiders
in rhythm and rhyme,

For the rhythm I find
the Love does impart,
it vibrates the meaning
direct to your heart.

Once your heart opens
then so does your mind,
you imbibe in that instant
the meaning opined.

And if that true meaning
comes straight from your soul,
it carries a message
that makes you feel whole.

And once you feel whole
then you know you are blessed.
So, if you are wise,
you'll let God do the rest.

Shaming your soul

Dorothy: 'Shalom to you today. I feel excited to be here even though my time is rather short. It is a pleasure to be in your company once again.'

Librarian: 'Shalom, and the pleasure is mutual. I am aware that your time is rather limited today but I am curious, what would you say your signal is that I am here waiting?'

Dorothy: 'I thought about that earlier in our meditation as it was a subject that was discussed between my partner and his inspirer last night. Today as I went into that meditation I saw the clearest green light, like green obsidian, sparkling like a river and thought that were I to follow that it would take me to the threshold. I also felt my third eye pulsating and I feel anticipatory.'

Librarian: 'Interesting and a good description given that we have never spoken about this. Green, of course, is predominate in your aura and so that is often projected within the mind's eye during meditation. But sensing a need to follow it is the key and also, I know, you were struck by its sparkle and clarity which I think you found new?'

Dorothy: 'True, I did wonder about that as every so often the colour that greets me is more like the green of Chalcedony, which is more opaque and has a blueish tinge to it. I find that calming, whereas this morning the green Light was energising.'

Librarian: 'What are you reading into the clarity and the sparkle?'

Dorothy: 'That perhaps things are clearing a little and that I am on the right path, so to speak. I certainly feel more at peace and get so much out of our conversations, although if I'm honest, I am still cautious about feeling too pleased with myself.'

Librarian: *Laughs.* 'That's wise, so many people use a little inspiration to make all kinds of claims and find themselves trapped in believing that they are more than they are. There is a difference for me however of proceeding with caution and allowing caution to stop the proceedings, or limit them.

'Last night your partner's inspirer talked about freedom, as have I with you. It is your next step, but it is an entirely internal step which needs no external proclamation or announcement. A step that you have already taken but do not believe it yet, and it is a step I took with you. It is, you might say, the leap of faith that so many speak of.'

Dorothy: 'My eyes are filling with tears, I don't know what to say.'

Librarian: 'Say more, what are you feeling at this moment?'

Dorothy: 'Fear, relief, anticipation, gratitude, anxiety.'

Librarian: 'That's quite a list, but not unexpected, for anyone to be ready to speak their Truth, even to themselves, is quite a step. Some people talk so easily about "being a child of God," but what does that really mean if you do not then find a way to express that magnificent Light in a world that so needs it, but fears it?

'What does it mean if you have not already struggled with surrendering your freewill over and again and then forgetting and claiming it back when it suits you — like a suitcase you retrieve from lost property?

'So few people are willing to consider what imbibing the Light of Spirit even means. If you accept it is intelligent, healing, and Loving, and yet without sentiment. And that it follows Universal Law without deviation, then surely it follows that imbibing that Light and seeking to follow it, presents challenge after challenge whilst in life?

'Denying this is shaming for your soul because your soul knows your struggles, past and future. It knows your true progress and when the personality denies, or inflates, that progress it shames your soul for it obscures the Truth. And yes, you were right to consider whether the sparkles within your green river were indicative of progress. You are correct, but as always they come without a fanfare and can diminish if your fears take hold or your personality seeks sole ownership.

'Spiritual progress is the purview of your soul and your soul alone, it cannot be owned, sold or bargained with. It is as gentle as your green river and it flows to the sea. You never swim alone for I am beside you, as are your other inspirers, and we all come from the same Source and have the same destination. And should you pause for a moment, you will see the Christos Light sparkling within every droplet.

'Shalom to you this day, I hope I have been brief enough.'

Dorothy: 'You have, thank you so much.'

Changes in humanity

Librarian: 'Beloved one, shalom to you this day, I sense a peace and a settling that was not present yesterday.'

Dorothy: 'Shalom and I do feel relief that the inauguration of a new President of the USA went well yesterday. There was no violence, his first speech touched on humanity and unity and his approach is inclusive, not divisive, which such is a relief.

'Every day at the moment seems to be about navigating risk and worrying about the continuation of the virus and its impact on the society in which I live. I wouldn't say I'm fearful but I am cautious and, thanks in large part to D's ongoing work and his saving regime over the last few years, I can make choices to avoid risks where others cannot. We can afford to eat well and heat our home. But oh my heart goes out to those who have to work with the sick, the elderly and the dying. I worry about the guilt that younger people may feel if they should feel responsible for the death of another. Whether some might experience lifelong sadness about their actions, or regret about acting recklessly, as that seems such a burden to have to carry.'

Librarian: 'That is the consequence, I am sorry to say, of the disregard generations of people have had for the Laws of life. And by this, I do not mean the man-made laws, but the fundamental principles of existence, one of which is the interconnectedness of all things.

'This is the inheritance that the young bear, and it is the collective karma that they have come to assuage. Although you are seeing it family by family, it is collective and it will be the making not only of this generation but of generations to come.

'You mentioned the compassion in the new President, and he in particular has absorbed that compassion through the painful loss of loved ones, greatly helped by his faith in something greater. This is in sharp contrast to the outgoing President who feared failure over everything else and felt he was special and fated to lead. His cast iron belief in individuality separated him not only from his self compassion but also his compassion for others and that, for him, is going to be a very difficult path indeed in the months to come.

'It is a painful truth that people only truly learn from experience, from the events where they see the error for themselves, where they personally experience emotions and where their hearts open to the suffering of others. You cannot teach, or learn by rote, how it feels to suffer or watch others suffer. And just as souls need to incarnate to experience life and assuage karma, so humanity has to experience the consequences of their actions and attitudes and yes, it can be painful indeed.

'But just as you fear now for the young who realise, perhaps too late, that their actions and attitudes affected others negatively, as the virus recedes that innate memory of connection will remain. It will embed itself in societies around the world and will become a more conscious conduit for Light and compassion. There will be a greater understanding of how your structures, that mirror the interconnectedness of the universe, can be misused.

'The connections are neutral, it is how society interprets them that matters. That is why the attitudes of your Leaders matter, for it sets a tone that like a virus infects the way people see both themselves and others. That is why you were affected by political events across your world, they do have an impact, they do resonate across the world.

'The virus that you are navigating could easily be seen as a metaphor for the changes that need to be established if mankind is to survive. It shows, does it not, how something does not need to be visible to be potent. How the actions of one affect the whole, how something intangible with built-in intelligence of its own can mutate to meet changing circumstances and acts without fear or favour. How, if something is purpose-driven, its gentle strength will prevail until that purpose fulfilled.

'All these things, and so much more, can be applied to the transmission of Light, Love, and peace within mankind. How the energy of God, if accepted by the collective, would transform the quality of life for humanity and for the planet itself. How that energy would re-connect people to their souls once again, so they would never feel separate again. There will come a time when the soul of humanity will be their guiding force, and that indeed will bring the peace you so desire. Such beauty is just within reach, the Bearers of Light have been sent as beacons and you have your words and those of others pointing the way. Let us pray that the eyes and hearts of mankind are more finely tuned to the approaching Light now that they are peering out of such darkness.'

The custodian of promises

Librarian: 'Beloved one I hear you for I never sleep, nor neglect my duties, they are my lifeblood as your thoughts and feelings are yours. As you toss and turn in the night I listen to your dreams, to your waking thoughts and images and I to the great wheels of progress turning on your planet. I absorb the tides of the sea and the tides of mankind, wave upon wave, hope and fear, loss and gain and I send my Love and I wait. I wait for you as I always wait for the hands of mankind to reach up, for they are always grasped, always met with tenderness and care, and when they don't reach up I reach down that bit farther. My head and my shoulders breaking through clouds in an attempt to help, to share wisdom and Love and bring memories of home and promises to God.

'You see me as a Librarian of Lives. You could see me as a custodian of promises, promises between souls and God, promises made in earnest, made with hope and acceptance, filled with the Love of God and the following wind of Spirit.

'So many promises lie dashed on your seashores, overcome by commerce, fear, and survival. I watch my charges, my beautiful charges, limp under burdens that are of the world and blind to the wind of Spirit in their lungs and filling their heart. Defeated by the density of life, without hope, heads down unable to see the golden hands of help reaching down. Fearful of reaching back to their memories of the lives that led to the promises they made and the purpose that sent them forth.

'So imagine my joy when one such as yourself not only reaches up, but listens too. Stays awhile amongst the living world of promises and hope and purpose and does her best to record what she feels in images that others might relate to. Someone who has reached a point of stillness within that can open to the vibrancy of the unseen world around her and send out tentacles of understanding. Tentacles that return to her world bringing peace and Love, stillness and wonder. Tentacles that bring back the promise God made to every soul He sent forth, "That they are loved, they have their place and there will be a welcome for them when they return". But more than that the golden cord that keeps them connected to their soul is a conduit of Light that only they can turn off. If they trust in the Light, it will trust in them and all will be well.

'Those are the promises I am a custodian to, the vibrant living souls, each with its part to play in the tapestry of life and the ultimate achievement of us all, which is to be absorbed back home.'

Planet in despair

Our planet is in deep despair
as our waste is everywhere.
It's in our seas and rivers too,
what is our Earth supposed to do?

Tolerate our sheer neglect?
Forgive us all our disrespect?
No, our betrayal must be halted,
greed on Earth is too exalted.

We, the architects of fate,
must take action, not too late.
For we alone are those who can
repair the ravages of man.

Vulnerability

Librarian: 'Come walk with me this morning, over misty paths towards the sea. Hear the gulls overhead and the sea in the distance and taste the salt on your lips. Let the breeze wash over you as you walk and lift your eyes to the sky which is turning pink, grey and soft blue. Your feet are sure-footed on this sandy path, for it is familiar to you. Within your body you feel the path dip downward towards the sea, past the coarse grass of the dunes.

'Along the beach the sand turns wetter and you keep walking with purpose, looking up to see the deepening pink of the dawn sky and feeling the early morning sun on your cheeks, gentle now but full of promise. You keep walking on the wet sand, slower now and with more care as it takes more effort to raise your foot and you are carefully navigating the rocks and sharp shells, for you are carrying your shoes at your side.

'All the time you are heading out to sea, the tide is out and the distance is great, but you do not hesitate. Item by item, you remove your clothing until you are naked and carrying your clothes. You are alone, completely alone, with the birds and the sound of the sea and you feel free as you dive into the water, worrying not about your clothes or making the return journey. You allow the water to carry you away and embrace you with its rhythm, within its energy, which is so gentle. You turn onto your back and allow yourself to drift, eyes closed, aware of the colours of the dawn, the rise, and fall of the waves and the peace that enfolds you.'

Dorothy: 'That was lovely, thank you, a metaphor for these morning conversations. I feel so peaceful and unguarded when I enter this space.'

Librarian: 'I know and this is why any Spirit who is designated to Teach, or shall we just say talk, with one of their charges needs to understand the level of vulnerability that that person is embracing when they open to their soul and the Spirit realms. It is not often talked about, this duty of care I think you call it, that Spirit has towards mankind but within the Teaching Realms it is a fundamental lesson.

'We have spoken about how freewill is sacrosanct and that is a given, but the gentleness and care is a given also. You, and anyone who opens, is as vulnerable as a naked body alone in the sea. The tides and storms that can occur are caused not by winds but by untimely interventions, misspoken phrases that can

81

cause anguish long after the person has metaphorically left the beach and enrobed themselves in the protections of life.

'This is why your Teachers have been so careful in your development. Why the path you tread to the place of surrender is one that you know well. It has been placed there by minds far greater than yours and with such Love and tenderness you would weep. It is important to recognise this from time to time, that when the connection is pure and well-prepared there is complete safety for the bond is one of Love.

'But, as you know yourself, there are many false paths and harsh guidance given that can create ripples in that connection between soul and personality for years to come. The mere act of searching assiduously and being open to all that comes does not always lead to peace. But the Truth does, for the Truth comes gently on the wings of Love, like the warm sun rising from the embrace of a pink dawn.'

Dorothy: 'Once again thank you, that was lovely. As you were speaking I was watching the dawn that was indeed a deep pink, beautiful, and now, as I say Shalom, I am looking at the softest purple hue in the sky.'

Librarian: 'Shalom beloved one, shalom.'

Thought patterns

Dorothy: 'Shalom to you this morning and may I apologise in advance as I am likely to be disturbed during our conversation.'

Librarian: 'Do you think this will bother me? Am I a light switch that sheds no light when you flick the switch? You know better than that by now I hope? You introduce something here that I would like to comment on. The Worlds of Spirit and the realm of the Earth intertwine, there are points of access and merging, channels of communication and portals that exist through intention, the wheels of Creation and by Teachers and Masters. So, although your soul and your personality are distinct, they are interdependent throughout life. It has become accepted that the communication has to be initiated, shall we say, by mankind. There are some wonderful examples of screwed up eyes, uncomfortable seating arrangements and endless incantations that would indicate Spirit is like toothpaste that needs forcing through a small aperture.

'I would say that nothing could be further from the Truth, but that would not be entirely accurate. It is true that mankind has to initiate, or I would prefer to say give their conscious agreement to, the intervention of Spirit in their lives. For some that would not be appropriate nor necessary, for their path, shall we say, is more material than spiritual. But that does not mean that Spirit is inaccessible to them, nor that they could not choose to develop a closer relationship with Spirit if they chose to.

'For the spiritually minded, shall we say, the channel remains open, although under the control of the human being. You could, for example, ask me nicely to go away if you find me disturbing your sleep with my brilliant insights. Although, to be fair, if you were asleep I would have no such trouble as your soul would be filling the same armchair that you are now. So, should you be finding my commentary on a daily activity distracting, not only will I sense it, but if you asked me to step back I would immediately acquiesce and not be offended.

'Did you know that you and other healers when in a soul, or dream, state can be called on to give healing in your world?'

Dorothy: 'Yes I do, and that the after effects can often be felt on waking.'

Librarian: 'That's good, but this is a case in point. Although Spirit will use the resources that are willing to be used for the good of humanity, they / we will also respect the freewill of our charges. We understand that they may ask to be allowed to sleep, or concentrate, or even choose to turn away from the spiritual for a while. We are not insensitive to the fact that having a spiritual perspective, especially at this time in your world, can be depressing and make you feel sad, impotent, or frustrated. Unfortunately, those are exactly the emotions that you are here to feel, for those are the constant barriers in life that all must learn to overcome. We are not here to wipe away the frustrations of life just to accompany you and offer what we can when we can.

'If you sit down for ten minutes or ten hours we would find something mutually rewarding to commune on. If you could see what I see, your beautiful, complex aura, filled with feeling, ideas, relationships with others, concerns for your world, all engraved upon a tapestry of the past and an outline of your purpose, you would know that I, for one, will never be short of conversation. Never tardy in taking whatever opportunity I can to bring my Light to life.

'Remember that all of our conversations are two-way, and although the words I choose are mined from your vocabulary you do not shape them with your expectations, and for that, I am grateful. But, I do respond to your needs and the needs of your soul, even those unknown to you, and in doing so, I receive by giving. It is said I believe that there is no better gift than giving, and that is so true here. As I speak I see your aura respond, creating new patterns, and as they emerge from within you, they emerge into the world. A world that needs new patterns of thinking, new Light and new directions more than ever. So, I am so grateful to you, more than you could ever know.'

Dorothy: 'Thank you, I am left with images of holographic forms floating into the world, colourful, peaceful and intricate like snowflakes falling.'

Librarian: 'You are closer to the Truth than you realise, if your thoughts are real then, how are they real, how do they manifest? If you can see Light and colour and peaceful patterns falling and feel their effect, surely darkness follows the same pattern? I know it is too simplistic to say that darkness rises while Light falls, but it gives you an idea. Dark thoughts remain within the Earth realm because they are of a lower vibration than the Spirit realms, so they congregate as cloud-like structures which block out the Light of Spirit that falls constantly on your earth. When those thought forms contain Light, such as you have described, it becomes useful to mankind. It can initiate new thoughts and actions that build on that Light and so it grows.

'Remember the Light is always stronger than the darkness, one shaft of Light will brighten an entire sky and backlight the clouds highlighting the universe of Light beyond, yet within reach. I hear the doorbell, shalom to you this day.'

Unmasked

Dorothy: 'Shalom to you this day and may I say today has a special hue about it for I feel we have been formally introduced by another Teacher who spoke this morning. An acknowledgment which is so important to me as I love and trust this Teacher completely. It is as if I met you at some function and although we have been happily chatting away we have not been formally introduced before today. So, a special good morning to you.'

Librarian: *Laughing.* "Shalom to you beloved one, shalom. I am laughing not at you, but at the difficulty of Spirit and man, or woman, communicating and trusting. There you are pleased to meet me and yet, I have known you your whole life and even before that. We have spoken together many times, not captured on your screen like now, but writ large in your soul and what you have said to me is writ large on mine too and yet, you do not know it.

'I am not insulted, or surprised, I am just very grateful to the Teacher who introduced us formally, you might say and for your trust in him, otherwise we might still be talking incognito, would we not? I know you have christened me "The Librarian" and I see no reason to change that nomenclature as it is descriptive of what I do and what I bring.

'We do not have names in the Spirit realms, we recognise each other by the patterns and colours of our auras. What you did when you named me was intuited what the patterns in my aura represent, even though you were unaware of doing so. There is always a place where imagination and intuition combine to make a clear representation of the unseen forces in life.

'I believe that in your earlier meditation you saw a different colour than usual when feeling our signal, is that right?'

Dorothy: 'Yes, I saw a beautiful mid-blue this morning which moved like waves.'

Librarian: 'And what did you think at the time?'

Dorothy: 'That that was the colour of intellect, of understanding, and I wondered if that was an indication that you might have information to impart.'

Librarian: 'That's interesting because you intuited information and then it came, not through me but through your other beloved Teacher. It is good to learn the language of colour and to start to recognise that it is a language and it is a universal language, not only between people but between Realms.

'Yesterday we spoke of the patterns made by thoughts and how the particles of thought, if I can call them that for clarity, are cohered by the universal mind, and given substance by the mind of human beings. You are aware of the Temples of Learning within the Spirit realms and of the need for souls to be active in order to continue to learn, adapt and change. They do not do that alone, they gather and create holographic images which provide what they need to learn. Perhaps, for example, a group of souls may be charged with working out how to respond to a crystal stratum on earth that has become dull and unresponsive.

'The closest I can come to describing how our activity might look to a visitor from earth would be experimental. But, we do not have huge laboratories with bubbling cauldrons or magnificent tubular structures like organ pipes spewing out steam and smoke as potions bubble and ferment under the watchful gaze of white coated men and woman.

'We congregate together to examine and explore events on the earth and to understand what needs to evolve and change. To achieve this we build representations of the problems we are seeking to resolve, be that the lack of energy within a crystal stratum, a new medical procedure that is being advanced on earth, or some analysis of why your fruits and vegetables no longer provide the same level of nutrients.

'If you could wander throughout the Spirit realms so many of the forms of learning would be familiar to you, except they are transparent and translucent as we work with the Light before it is released to mankind. And when it is released it is quality checked, you might say, to ensure that Love coats each particle. Every thought pattern that is released must respect the supremacy of the Christos Light. In Truth, it would not be possible to interfere with the Christos Light because that is the fundamental building block of life itself. We take great care to ensure that the evolution of any idea, or initiative, is thought through and every possible outcome provided for.

'Mankind has always pitted evolution against Creation and this is surprising to us. Surely, when man manufactures something they make allowances and predictions about what it will need to keep functioning. You could produce the most beautiful car, for example, with sleek body work and capable of incredible speeds, but no one would buy it if you could not replace the tyres, or reach into the engine to repair it. Why then would The Creator not make contingency plans for the human body against changes in climate, or provide animals with the need to evolve when their food sources dry up? It's inconceivable that a mind as great as one that could encapsulate Creation would not think a long, long way ahead. Indeed, as the Creator is beyond time then the full life cycle of everything would already be known would it not?'

Dorothy: 'True, the Creation v Evolution argument is always one I have avoided, partly because it evokes such strong reactions and is so polarised. It makes sense to me that everything evolves. I found anatomy and physiology awe-inspiring. As I learnt about the human body I was amazed at its complexity, the forethought, or inspiration, behind each system and its ability to adapt, let alone its interaction with all other living systems. Unfortunately, the teacher was lousy and so maintaining that level of awe was difficult, I could not understand why it did not inspire her.'

Librarian: 'And all with the power of thought; patterns of Light imbued with the intelligence and Love of God and released into mankind. A trinity represented by Yeshua, the Christ, and replicated in every living being in your world.

'It is a pleasure to meet you beloved one, no longer masked strangers at a ball, but unmasked and happy to dance together. Shalom.'

The soul of humankind

When from the Realms of Silence
a few pearls do descend,
don't cast them off like raindrops,
accept them like a friend.

For Spirit's Love for mankind
is as deep as it is wide.
A patient and abiding Love
that never will subside.

It's in the act of healing,
in a smile, or sunlit morn.
It's in the eyes of children
celebrating being born.

It is the soul of humankind,
that soft and gentle glow,
that radiance you feel, not see,
yet truly, truly, know.

Is this hangover?

Librarian: 'Shalom to you this day and you had a busy night I feel?'

Dorothy: 'Shalom and yes, my dreams have been vivid these last few nights and I wonder if that is to do with these conversations. I don't think the dreams are of interest in themselves, but I am certainly waking up a little exercised. We could have been dancing all night at the unmasked ball, of course, and this could just be a hangover.'

Librarian: 'An interesting choice of words beloved one seeing that neither of us drink nor dance, except metaphorically with our thoughts and feelings. I don't believe in the long history of spiritual encounters that the chosen description would be of dancing at a ball and getting a hangover but, and this may not surprise you, there is some Truth in your statement.

'In the last few weeks you have not just crossed the threshold, picked up a portion of peace and Light, said thank you, and departed. You have engaged with the thoughts and Teachings, you have been open and shared with me. I'd like to think that with all my years of experience and accumulation of knowledge that what I say not only has Truth within it, but awakens the Truth within those I talk to. So, you are not passive, when we are consciously communicating your mind is expanding and reorienting long after we have spoken. A hangover if you like, but one you won't be curing anytime soon with a raw egg.'

Dorothy: *Laughing.* 'And one I have no desire to find a cure, I am finding this enticing and exciting.'

Librarian: 'There you go, back to your ball metaphor, which again has Truth within it. A ball, at least in my imagination, has colour, light, and movement within it. Everyone has to chose their path through a multitude of possibilities and invitations, and the patterns that they create are complex, some familiar and some new. Each person has to navigate a path, shine in their own way, if they want to be noticed, and join in with the patterns and rhythm if they are not going to stand out.

'When we speak we are one channel within what you have named the Library of Lives, a vibrant Realm of movement, colour and Light, where every soul has to find their place and absorb the new rhythm of life here. For some that is shocking and unexpected, for others it has been a long time coming. So do you see the similarities?'

Dorothy: 'Yes, yes I do and I imagine that on a subconscious level, I am picking up some of these patterns of re-entry shall we say?'

Librarian: 'Indeed so, for the struggles that the homecoming souls have on arrival bear the density of life and that will naturally attract some of your attention, even though you may think your focus is entirely on me. Of course, your presence brings a density that is familiar and attractive to them so, as we are speaking, there are a series of minute, instantaneous and subconscious exchanges happening and they leave a subconscious impression on you. In the same way as watching the news does when the information is distressing and you witness others experiencing pain, grief or loss.

'It is no coincidence that in the last couple of days you have been reaching out to people in your community who are suffering, for your sensitivity to that field of energy has been energised by our conversations. I hope that does not discourage you?'

Dorothy: 'Of course not, I don't think anything will do that. I am having two reactions to your explanation, firstly it explains a lot and I am happy to know what's happening, secondly it sounds so fantastical I am arguing with my imagination again.'

Librarian: *Laughing.* 'Well we have gone from dancing all night to our first argument it seems, is that a domestic?'

Dorothy: 'I'm not really arguing, but taking some time to let in the information without immediately dismissing it as fantasy.'

Librarian: 'Then beloved one we are going to have more domestics because the beautiful complexity of the Spirit realms is impossible to describe. Your soul has not left the Spirit realm it inhabits, but your memory of it while in life is not available to you. You have gone further than many in finding comparable metaphors to explain the unexplainable, and for that, I applaud you, but you're right no soul arrives home obese with the actual density of life. However, it is filled with the memories of life and perhaps some pain or trauma, and they ease this transition by the recreating familiar, healing, surroundings where they feel closer to their loved ones. This does create a denser pattern than those created by the souls who have advanced in the Spirit realms and shed their Etheric body.

'When we speak the two Realms we inhabit are drawn closer and the veil thins. I become more aware of the density of life while you are speaking, of your surroundings, at least your reaction to them and of the pull of nature and the wider world. So, it makes sense that you too are aware of the wider field of Love, colour and Light that I inhabit and become accustomed to the movements within it. There are souls that do gather to listen to our conversations because I have something of a reputation as a Teacher, you might say. They may be preparing for a life on earth, perhaps attentive to a growing foetus, so being close to our conversations is a gift, a porthole into life and the difficulties mankind have in accepting their collective relationship with the Spirit world. That's not so different from a grand ball, is it?'

Dorothy: 'That has put a shiver down my spine, we are expecting a granddaughter this summer and the thought that she might be listening in is too much to contemplate. That would be beyond marvellous.'

Librarian: 'Do you not think that the incarnating souls take an active interest in the country they have chosen or in the family? Do you think that they would limit their observations and knowledge to their chosen parents alone? Every soul chooses carefully and this is particularly true for the offspring of the Bearers of Light for they bear great wisdom and knowledge, not only from the past but of the future too. Should mankind remain blinkered, they know the consequences and their purpose within that and they embrace it eagerly before birth as well as after.

'She will need your support and your love which I know you, and your partner, have in abundance and she knows that too.'

Dorothy: *Cries.*

Librarian: 'I trust those are tears of joy and that you allow this Light in, you know its Source and its heart. Shalom to you this day, shalom.'

Prayer

Within my head my prayer was spoken,
each gap was filled with Light.
And as I watched tendrils of colour
wove a pattern in my sight.

I saw them reach out far beyond me,
on paths they knew so well.
And as they plaited in formation
their vibrancy did swell.

Their colour palette was exquisite,
pastels, jewels and pearls.
I was breathless as I witnessed
the power of prayer unfurl.

The words themselves were punctuations,
that cohered the flow of Light.
It is the energy of heart,
that gives all prayers their might.

Changes are afoot

Librarian: 'Shalom. I do believe this is our one-month anniversary, a full moon cycle of speaking almost every day. We now have a greater understanding and confidence in each other and a growing anticipation of continuing, both of which bring me pleasure.'

Dorothy: 'Yes I think you're right, our first conversations were at the end of the last calendar year and now it is almost the end of January.'

Librarian: 'And things are beginning to quieten down in your country from the virus, are they not?'

Dorothy: 'Yes, they are, and unseemly arguments are now breaking out about who gets the vaccine and who does not in the UK and Europe. It is as if the lessons from the pandemic are already fading, as commercial considerations and protectionism are on the rise again. But perhaps I can say that when I have an appointment booked for the vaccine, although that does not feel to me like a "Get out of jail free" card.

'My greatest fear at this time is that the opportunities within the pandemic will be lost, although I cannot see how life could possibly return to normal when so many businesses have failed and fear is on the rise. I know that fundamental change is needed, but I cannot envisage how it will look, and that scares me because I don't know how to cooperate with what I cannot see.'

Librarian: 'Then I am the fortunate one! You cooperate with me when you cannot see me, you have followed channelled Teachings for years, it seems to me that finding the threads within the great spirals is something you are good at. I know that in your earlier meditation you spoke about it being the full moon and the great wheels of Light that affect humanity and all upon your planet. Do you think it was a coincidence that we started speaking as these wheels turned and produced opportunities for change, an opportunity that you have grasped with both hands?

'I do agree that mankind seems intent on ignoring the movements and forgoes the opportunities for a reset, shall we say, in favour of the known. But it is in sitting rooms like this and in conversations like ours all over the globe that the threads of change will be woven together. The Bearers of Light, like you, have had time on their hands, time to reflect, and an internal prompt to find ways of acting in the world that will remove the blinkers.

'There is growing anger amongst the young because the inequalities of life have been laid bare through the pandemic, they have suffered loss and hardship and many see their anticipated futures fading before their eyes. What so many were working towards no longer seems possible, or even acceptable, to them and out of that anger will come a sense of power, an imperative to change. They will begin to weave the threads of Light from the great spirals into new ways of living, new ways of working, and will work with the Bearers of Light to create new futures for themselves and the planet.

'They will need support, to know that there are others who have trodden some of these paths before them. Others brave enough to know that while they might not know the destination they are happy to trust that the collective Light of mankind, once awake, can and will create a better, fairer and freer world for all.

'Within the loss and the grief of the pandemic is the space needed for humanity to grow. The lessons that need addressing are writ large, and within the spiritual hearts of those who pray, meditate, listen and follow the threads of spiritual Light is hope, not just for themselves but for humanity. By believing in this you, and others, can energise those threads of Light and enable them to vibrate against the cheeks of the young who have come for this very purpose.

'You don't have to do anything other than cooperate with the changes. They will be organic, some will be painful, but they will transform this world in a way that would make you weep with joy, were you to live to see it, but your granddaughter will. There is your future, there are the threads of Light that you need to add your Light to, and the marvel of this? You don't even have to leave your sitting room!'

Dorothy: 'That's good I think I may have forgotten how to open the garden gate. Thank you, once again. Shalom.'

Early morning musings

Librarian: 'I am here beloved one, I am here. Shalom to you. Listen to your sleeping world, the peace that settles, the nighttime workers in the distance, the babies crying, the trains running. Your city lit up in red and white as empty offices wait, not just for morning but for a return to normality, whatever that might be.

'Your hospitals full of people unable to breathe, frightened, with tired doctors and nurses tending machines and wiping away their fears and the fears of those they care for. Think of the souls no longer laying in a hospital bed but here now, many so exhausted from their fight, aching over the distance between them and their loved ones.

'Watch for a moment and what do you see?'

Dorothy: 'First I see collections of animals, dogs wagging their tails, cats, horses, birds flying, then I notice a reunion between a bird of prey and a man who seemed to arrive with his arm already outstretched. There are many, many cats who are weaving through legs and people, not as demonstrative as the dogs, but nestling between legs and being raised into arms.

'But I also see people standing dazed and confused, looking around, some silently arguing with themselves, some cross as if they should not be here. They look like someone who has arrived at a bus stop having just watched their bus pull away. Some are standing as if on a cold day flapping their arms to keep warm and working faster and faster as they realise their arms have no substance to them.

'But, and this is emotional, I also see each person has been met by a Being of Light, gentle, patient and completely calm. They are standing close by and as other souls approach they stand back a little way but take up a watching brief. Now I see human forms and shapes appear, family and ancestors I assume, for they are not all of this day and Age. Some are greeted with immediate recognition and enthusiasm, for some it takes longer as if their Etheric form is not recognisable to the homecoming soul. Occasionally, there is some hesitation.

'The role of the Light Beings is so fascinating, they are so confident and assured as they guide people one way or another and take care of those who remain alone, perhaps through shock. They walk with them towards beaches, gardens, rivers, and homes as if they are invited guests. From what you have said, I imagine that these places have been created by the homecoming souls because they are familiar and soothing. I see rooms in intricate detail, gardens, mountain views and beaches and people standing or sitting in them. Alone, as far as I can see after the initial reunions have been completed, but in the care of this Being, who sits, or stands, completely still in their presence but their attention is palpable, gentle, and loving.

'It is a beautifully choreographed ballet in a way and it makes me feel sad.'

Librarian: 'Why, can you say more?'

Dorothy: 'Because if this is true, if it exists beyond my imagination, then it is a tragedy that people fear death so much, it really does feel like a threshold to another world of opportunity and life. There is so much life here, all of it gentle, ordered and peaceful.'

Librarian: 'There is Truth in your imaginings as your feeling of sadness attests, but remember, that homecoming souls arrive into the Realm that their way of life has earned for them. A Being of Light meets everyone and most people, have reunions with their loved ones that have predeceased them, but there is learning too and although that comes only from the soul it can be difficult.

'The most difficult lesson, in my estimation, is regret for things not done, for opportunities not taken, for realising that that gentle nudge of Spirit that you ignored for so long was pointing you in the direction of achievement. Real achievement, not wealth, or ambition, but Love, purpose and fulfilment.

'Although your imagery reflects the peaceful homecoming of so many, often uneventful, lives spent caring for others, or in service in some way, there are also some souls for whom an embrace of Light and Love would be too challenging. You have had to achieve some degree of spiritual acceptance in life to be able to open to the Light, which gets brighter gradually. It is never too late, to open to Spirit in life, until you draw your last breath it is never too late.'

Dorothy: 'Strange is it not that we start talking about the sleeping city at 3am and move in to the world of Spirit? It seems as if the city is empty of people and the Spirit world is full, now that would seem so crazy to so many.'

Librarian: 'It is in times of emptiness that you can travel in your mind and begin to explore other Realms, other possibilities. You can sit in stillness and intuit the movement in the surrounding air, the calls, and cries of those departing your world for mine. The movement of the energy of your earth and the planets moving in their orbits, peacefully, powerfully and intelligently. You can begin to wonder at the intelligence beyond your own realm and imagine what "knowing" might mean for life on the Realms that encircle your Earth.

'We talked yesterday about the pandemic and what it might mean for humanity. Your empty streets and offices, the stillness and reflection that is more abundant, the re-balancing of priorities, all of this is a side effect, a consequence of a light switch being flicked off in some invisible Realm. Although so many see only the loss of Light some, see the Light rising behind your tall buildings and a soft, pink dawn emerging edged with gold.

Dorothy: 'Who flicked the Light switch?'

Librarian: 'Mankind did, but it was not one flick of one switch, it was billions of flicks of the wrist as they turned their attention towards themselves and away from the planet and the Light that sent them forth. It is an irony is it not that now a light switch has been metaphorically switched off across your towns and cities mankind has given more of their attention to the Light that can never be extinguished. The Light that lives in your hearts and needs only your stillness and belief to emerge from the shadows once more.'

Dorothy: *Smiles.* 'So here's to many more early mornings then.'

Librarian: 'And many more with the courage to explore what that stillness tells them and to act on their emerging Light. Shalom to you, peace be with you.'

Soul

I'm no more than a thought away,
as you traverse your earth's short stay.
I harvest all your riches earned,
each precious lesson that you've learned.

I am the Light within your eyes,
I am the force of Love that ties
you to purpose, meaning too,
expressing it in all you do.

And when, at times, you turn away,
I nestle quietly, I still stay.
That silent, patient, loving, voice,
that honours you and your free choice.

And when, at times, we do commune,
I bring to you my own sweet tune.
The eternal Aum that never fades,
and with pure peace your heart invades.

The Tree of Life

Librarian: 'Ah, welcome, come sit awhile and drink your tea. Life feels busy does it not and yet, you are so still these days.'

Dorothy: 'Yes it does and the stillness is not entirely internal, I barely leave the house these days, but still life seems busy.'

Librarian: 'That is because your mind is reaching out and up all the time. The daily cycle of news and events that you follow has taken on another dimension, one that strangely drives you more towards your soul and its perspective on life. But the perspective of a soul can feel callous to a human being watching their brothers and sisters struggling and in pain. On one level, you know that the cleansing cannot be stopped and change must come, but you are witnessing the birth pangs. No one who has been through childbirth can witness a child being born without a tear in their eye and a wide open heart.

'Living life with an open heart can be a challenge. The walls of your home provide protection, not just a physical one against the virus, but a psychic one too, this enables your own development to continue at speed. For this is what this is, your personal development, you are taking the place that has been waiting for you since the moment of your birth. A place that has been prepared with great care and Love and needs you as much as you have needed to find your way closer to your soul and to the Realm that it inhabits.'

Dorothy: 'It does feel like a homecoming in some ways, although I always know when it is time to return. I realised that many times when I first read spiritual Teachings I would shrug my shoulders as if to say. "Well I knew that already, there's nothing new". It was as if I understood the words and the construction of the sentences, but the true meaning took much longer to embed within me.'

Librarian: 'Can you give me an example?'

Dorothy: 'I thought you might ask that … I think my early understanding of spiritual Love is an example. Phrases like, "God loves you," are familiar, but I interpreted that like the love of a parent where you could discuss, argue and navigate a pathway that suited you. I now know that God's Love is unbending, non-sentimental and unconditional and it cannot be bargained with. It stands for what is best for your soul and you like it or lump it.'

Librarian: 'That is a good example because statements about the Spirit world being patient and loving and freewill being sacrosanct all weave into an understanding, or misunderstanding, of the phrase, "God Loves you". Now you might ask who is the "you" in that statement, your personality, or your soul, and does it matter? Does there come a time when eternal patience and making freewill sacrosanct start to feel less like Love and more like indifference? After all if God is indifferent, then does It Love you or even care about you at all?

'How can there be a true understanding of that phrase for anyone who denies their soul, for how else does God express Love except to the personality via the soul? How far down the spiritual path do you need to be to even think about soul and personality and whether one is the vessel for the other?

'This is all before we consider the impact of freewill and the apparently perverse learning that can come from denying God's Love, or feeling unworthy of it. And all this from three words — God Loves you — constantly repeated and exhorted by many desperate to believe it themselves, or find a way to self forgiveness or any sense of value in a personality fighting itself.'

'This is what I mean by you finding your way here, to your place and even though it is not your final destination, there are Realms, even reams, of learning still to come. Perhaps, just perhaps, having an experience of God's Love is a staging post in its own right? You have the lived experience of the two sides of the coin, the deep and unconditional, patient Love, and the feeling of being dispensable, insignificant, and unloveable. You have the experience of turning away and turning towards, and of knowing the landscape you walk each time you turn your head. You know what those words mean intellectually, emotionally and physically and your soul sings because it feels Loved and it knows that that Love is immutable and can be relied upon.'

Dorothy: 'That is all very true, and perhaps coincidentally I chose as an example the most fundamental lesson I needed to learn first so that all the other layers of learning had a foundation on which to build.'

Librarian: 'It was no coincidence beloved one, think of the tree of life for God's Love is the trunk and the sap. You may write the words, tattoo them on your body, exhort them from a pulpit, but until you know that is the sap that fills you then it is nothing more than words on a page. Understandable as text, but whose true meaning escapes you until you have experienced the Light that fills them. Shalom to you this day and peace be with you.'

The compact

Dorothy: 'Shalom to you, earlier today we were discussing thresholds and you and I have talked about this before. My partner's inspirer described the bridge between mankind and Spirit as the threshold of eternity, that evoked the feeling I have when I visit, even though I can barely explain what I mean by visit.

Librarian: 'Why don't you try.'

Dorothy: 'Well after I have sounded an Aum and said my prayer I sense a stilling, a depth within, which enfolds me and then I start to listen to see if you are there.'

Librarian: 'As opposed to?'

Dorothy: 'I don't know, elsewhere I suppose, busy with something else.'

Librarian: 'Well let's assume for the sake of this description that my mind is never too full, or too engaged elsewhere, to be attentive to your call, for I am always present during your meditations. You both have quite a band of helpers you know, for the purpose of those meditations is healing, of both individuals and the earth, as well as the imparting of knowledge. Your sounding of the Aum and prayer alerts Spirit and together we create a spiral of Light that contains a magic ingredient — the intention and energy of mankind — which is then directed to those areas most in need. It is a very cooperative affair and one which we all look forward to.

'So the pump is primed, you might say by the time you sit down, although describing myself as a pump might not be the most flattering description of myself.'

Dorothy: *Laughs.* 'I assume you are long past the stage where descriptions bother you, you must be far too certain of who you are and what you stand for.'

Librarian: *Laughing.* 'Correct. Now you might think that is because I lack ego, or have moved beyond it, but in fact it is because I have accepted the Sacred Laws. I abide by them and if I had a body, they would be my skeleton and my heart. That, and this may surprise you, gives me great freedom and confidence to be who I am. I love, I am intrigued by, Creation. I know I have a part to play and I do so willingly. I love the fact that I do not know everything that there are still some aspects of Creation to explore and discover. I even marvel at the unintended consequences of freewill because that throws up problems that great minds, far greater than mine, have to monitor and decide whether to step in to deflect mankind from doing something that would be catastrophic to itself.'

Dorothy: 'How can Spirit intervene in anything humanity does, does that not go against the Law that freewill is sacrosanct?'

Librarian: 'In all situations, perhaps particularly those where the outcome could be catastrophic, there is freewill in action on both sides, consciences are pricked and different opinions and arguments rage. One example would be the build up to a nuclear war. At this time, no one person could act alone or be unaware of the consequences, so it is through debate, discussion and the energising of conscience that Spirit can, and does, act, or sometimes through the intercession of prayer. The depth of Love Spirit has for mankind and the planet is beyond description. There is never a time when we are not intertwined with all the actions of mankind, all of them, even those apparently done in secret in some hidden cave or dungeon. Nothing is unknown to us, and there is nowhere that Love fears to tread.

'So in truth you do not need to call me, or step up, over, or onto a threshold where I immediately rush to greet you, I am in your being and you are in mine. I had to be accepted by you, I could not impose myself. So, when you talk about a stilling and a depth you are right there was a certain depth, or vibration, that you needed to reach to be able to hear me and once you did that created the connection. I could never turn away but you always can, although that would sadden me greatly.'

Dorothy: 'That does not bear thinking about, although with all privileges comes responsibility, so I hope I am up to the challenge.'

Librarian: 'Well your soul certainly did because it signed you up for this compact long before you were born and ... oh! Let me look more closely ... well, what do you know, there's your signature on the dotted line too.'

Dorothy: *Laughing.* 'So I suppose you're going to tell me that as the compact is written in Light and not on paper, it cannot be torn up.'

Librarian: *Laughing.* 'Precisely so. I think you get my meaning Dorothy Marsden you are as committed to me as I am to you and so it will ever be. Before you get too downhearted, may I point out that the compacts that go unfulfilled, ignored, or pushed onto the back burner until too late are the cause of more spiritual heartbreak than anything else. So, I think we should count you amongst the lucky ones, don't you?'

Dorothy: *Smiling.* 'Indeed so, it's been quite a journey so far, so I am looking forward to the next chapter.'

Personality & soul

Dorothy: 'Shalom. May I start with an experience I had on waking, where I felt myself to be just energy? At first, I saw a column but then I would describe it as a corkscrew movement, entering my body which was an empty, protective shell. The energy was me, ageless, complete, healthy, pure and so appreciative of slipping back into this warm shell. At that moment I thought of all the things people say about an ageing body, how the body ages but they still feel twenty years old. I felt great appreciation for my body, but I had this experience of being greater than it too, although that sounds a little too grand.'

Librarian: 'Interesting, I can see how real that experience was for you and I know that you felt your soul re-enter your body from its nightly sojourn in Spirit. This is one of the hidden benefits, you might say, of these discussions, your soul is feeling less constrained by your personality.

'It's hard to describe the interplay throughout life between the soul and the personality. Some would argue that the Soul is all knowing, and at Source and collectively that is ninety percent true. There is knowledge and intelligence that is not Soul-based, but the aggregate of all life experience and the spiritual knowledge of all the Masters, Prophets, and Sages rests within the Soul. The Soul is also aware of its interdependence with Planetary life, which is pure intelligence, and of the forces beyond itself which all abide within Sacred Law. It is beyond description really the field of intelligence in which all this exists, the harmony, the cooperation, the eternal movements of the Spheres and the great coordinating Field of thought that knows every molecule intimately.'

'It is no different with your body. This great mind is intimate with every cell, of every body on earth and yet, the energy force of every person is free to move beyond the body, to explore the spiritual Realms. This force, this soul, is never separate from Spirit and there are times when the soul seeks instruction, or respite, or peace from the personality which it inhabits. It is a personality that has been chosen by the soul for the purpose it has come to fulfil. The personality is like a carved figurehead at the bow of the vessel containing the soul, exposed to the tides and storms of life. It can become battered and worn long before the ship itself has sustained any real damage. It can become detached, broken and even mocked, or outdated as times change.

'As you know you awoke this morning to experience your soul's re-entry. We have spoken before about your soul's nocturnal visits and as you have grown in confidence in this Realm, so it follows that your soul feels that your personality is willing to let go of the leash that little bit more. Each time you visit here when awake and conscious, you have to involve your personality. You are, after all, not in a trance, you are conscious of the world around you, you can stop if you have to and reconnect when you need to. It is your personality that smiles as you close your computer satisfied with what you have written and often a little bemused at the way our conversations have developed.

'So your personality is, you might say, enjoying the journey that your soul is leading on and that has awakened it to the importance of your body as a vehicle that has served it well. It is more aware, shall we say, that the body is finite, but you are not and it is not, you bring your personality to the Library as I bring mine. How boring would it be if there was no personality within our discussions? No melding of the realities of our lives with the dry facts of the Spiritual Laws? No acknowledgement from me of the struggles and seeming impossibility of our tasks; mine in describing the indescribable and yours in believing the unbelievable. How many return visits do you think you would have made? I suggest very few without our personalities creating some equality between us. Some sense of a mutual struggle, of the potential for error on both sides, but an implicit agreement that we are in this together and Love is the bond.'

Dorothy: *Smiling.* 'That's so true, as always. I would not have even dared to think we are equal in any way. I think if I was trembling and in awe our conversations would have been shorter, fewer and less instructive in content.'

Librarian: *Laughing.* 'Beloved one, more souls than you could possibly count tremble before me. I am not certain whether they are in awe, certainly they are in shock because the path they all have to walk is the path to Love. A path that has been open to them their whole life long, but is now the single track they have to take. The gates fly open, Love beckons and they tremble.

'You do not tremble because you have come to know Love, as much by its absence as by its presence. You too and have a vessel to be grateful to, for your Masters and Teachers mapped out your journey here with great care and Love. They have walked in front, besides you and behind and carried you some of the way. To your credit you have run, walked, limped and listened, as you are listening now, and molecule by molecule Love has overcome doubt and fear and trepidation. You would think, would you not, that allowing Love in would be easy — but that it seems is no longer the way of mankind. But that will change, believe me beloved one, that will change.'

Beware false gods

Librarian: 'Beloved one shalom to you today and believe me I know. I know your thoughts and your feelings as you approach this work each morning, for work is what it is. There may be no currency changing hands, but there is an exchange every morning and as you approach you wonder what you have to barter with, often feeling it is nothing. But it is a great deal, your attention and your acceptance is a great deal and ... *cries* ... it brings me such joy.'

Dorothy: *Softly and with tears in her eyes.* 'I don't want to come with my emptiness and I don't want to come with my need, so I follow my feelings and come in trust. But it is hard knowing that there is so much I do not know, so much I do not have the language for, could I fail you?'

Librarian: 'When all is learning there is no failure, only the occlusion of the Light, and in that respect we are equal. I have my responsibilities which are to be as clear as I can and not to mislead and your responsibility is to listen as accurately as you can and forgo interpretations or censorship. Not easy, I know when you have spent three score years and ten in a world that uses censorship as a weapon. That, many generations ago, placed its survival and pleasure above everything else and actively disentangled governments from Spirit and Soul and placed financial gain in the place of God Itself.

'It is hard to open to Spirit, really open to Spirit. Where is that written in the self-help manuals that promise escape from the noise of life with a few deep breathing exercises? Or worse still the voices that proclaiming that salvation waits on another planet for the chosen few who pay for their passage by relinquishing their own freewill and common sense.

'What mankind seem unable to grasp is that God, however it may be portrayed or perceived, has already chosen every living being. He, or It, has equipped everyone with freewill, a conscience, intelligence, and an imperative towards Love — both through the desire body and through their soul connection — and a beautiful garden in which to live. None of this is conditional or comes weighed down with sanctions, it is given freely to the Collective Soul who requested it.

'And His expectations in return? That the Love that sent them forth is shared and returned. That the peace that sent them forth is honoured, and that no person seeks to stand above God in their treatment of another living being or thing.

'It is a beautiful, beautiful, Plan which can still play out on this planet if mankind wake up to their interdependence on all living things. Accepts their self responsibility to their own soul and the Soul of humankind and the gifts that everyone, everyone, has inside them. The gift of Light and Love is their handrail home individually and collectively.

'So, whether you come empty or full, sad or happy, anxious or elated it is your application of self responsibility and freewill that is important, not the outcome, or the product, but your surrender to the act of learning. The recognition of ignorance and the willingness to turn inward for sustenance and not to the world of false gods, which can only shame your soul and delay its fulfilment. There is no bartering over Love it is given freely and is returned in equal measure that, should anyone ever ask, is the universal "get out of jail free card".'

Dorothy: *Smiling.* 'Fair enough, until tomorrow then. Thank you and shalom.'

Librarian: 'Beloved one, shalom. If you should call on me this evening, I will not let you down. Shalom.'

Skating on thin ice

Librarian: 'Beloved one speak to me.'

Dorothy: 'I don't know what to say. I feel as if humanity is standing on cracking ice and peddling as hard as they, we, can trying not to succumb to the icy water underneath. I have not been able to keep peddling like my partner has, so much of my identity a year ago has slipped away and I have been complicit in this. So, what is left? This writing and these conversations which are a wonder and a delight and my family. My precious family, who I love more than I can say and even though they too are standing on the cracking ice I am trying to remain calm and trust they will survive and thrive.'

Librarian: 'Then we need to look up do we not? Your cracking ice, as I see it, is in the middle of a lake. The air is cold and the world is pregnant with fear. You see others trying to cross the lake, some well provided for with sleighs, dogs, and blankets while others slip and slide about in unsuitable clothes, praying they survive without falling too far or too badly.

'Standing still on cracking ice is not sensible, so you move slowly knowing that your journey is important, not just to you, but to those you care for. You stop to help those you can, steadying one another as you go, and your lack of balance causes you to laugh together. You begin to get a sense of the structure beneath your feet and work out how to identify the thinnest parts and how to manage your weight and the weight of others to avoid further cracking.

'You become attuned to the nature of the ice and begin to respect it and you are sensitive to the slightest movement in the air and any change in temperature. You are alert to the impact of others, most notably those adding weight with their equipment and their speed. You become aware of the stillness that embraces all this activity like a fall of fresh snow and of the birds flying freely high above you.

'Now and then you dare to pause for breath and look up at the sky, not sure what you are looking out for but allowing its cool blue to soothe you and steady your heartbeat. As you take in this calmness your gaze is drawn to the snow capped mountains that encircle the lake and they feel enticing, like monuments to all that is known, all that is safe. They seem to have a warm, magnetic energy all of their own, and you don't know why you have never noticed this before.

'You keep going, cautiously, aware of the danger you are in but surprisingly more alive and alert than when you were on the shore. You are attuned to nature and to humanity through the pores of your skin and the breath in your body and this sense of being alive and part of nature itself is exhilarating. You have a single focus at this moment and that focus is love and purpose and cooperation with all that is around you as that is how you will survive.

'Now, why have I painted this picture? I am sure you already know the answer, mankind is indeed standing on cracking ice and at this time many are either the victims of selfishness or the purveyors of it. The pandemic might be the headline, but the cracks within the fabric of society began many generations ago and could be ignored no longer. Mankind has been sleepwalking into disaster and has forgotten how to be truly alive, in harmony with nature and with one another through the pores of their skin and the air that they breathe.

'You can interpret the mountains in many ways, my preference would be that you see them as the fingers on the palm of God. And should your journey be one of purpose and Love then your passage, whilst not assured, will be one that will be in service of others.'

Dorothy: 'That was lovely, surprising as always, but lovely and with so much hope within it, that has lifted my spirits. Thank you.'

Librarian: 'Then I am pleased for my journey is no different from yours, purpose and Love are my watchwords too. Shalom to you this day, shalom.'

Vaccination day

Librarian: 'Beloved one I feel your fear, speak to me.'

Dorothy: 'Yes, I am due to have my vaccine today for Covid-19 and I am fearful. I realise it's not just the vaccination itself, but it's the journey too. I barely leave the house these days and so that in itself feels risky as I have to go to a hospital. I know it is my decision and I know it is early days in the development of the vaccine, but my boys are worried about me and really want me to have it. I feel it is the responsible thing to do not just for myself, but for any health worker who may have to care for me if I get sick. I realise I have mixed feelings and am scared.'

Librarian: 'My beloved one this is a case of too much knowledge being a difficulty and too little knowledge compounding the issue. This virus is a new kid on the block and it throws up challenges that need addressing urgently by humanity and so it will be wily as it moves to fulfil its purpose. You know in your heart that the vaccine is not a cure, and that the long-term impact of any vaccine produced so quickly cannot possibly be known at this time. But neither does anyone know the long-term effects of having the disease and recovering from it. You also have a precious grandchild on the way and I know that's an imperative that is close to your heart. So, your decision to have the vaccine is a balanced one given all that is known and all that is knowable at this point.'

Dorothy: 'My sons and daughter-in-law have just been in touch wishing me luck, so I know they're holding their breath for this. I feel that their needs are important too, not just my own.'

Librarian: 'When I talk of the virus fulfilling its purpose this is exactly what I mean. What better way of evoking humanity to turn away from selfishness than to feel, as you do, their deep concern that you act that they hope will protect you. They do not see themselves as separate from you, even though you have barely spent any time together for months now, the love that binds you and the future generation is strong indeed. If that understanding was commonplace, then all humanity would be thriving. There would be more respect, cooperation, and consideration between people and the concept of everyone being brothers and sisters under one sun would be realised.

'I am not saying that this virus is a deliberate act from a Higher Source, do not misunderstand me. I am saying that it is the net result of a lack of humanity amongst mankind. I talked earlier about no one knowing the long-term impact of the vaccine, well, the way in which this virus replicates is a visible and painful outworking of the choices that humanity have made over generations. Choices made without any thought of the consequences on themselves, or their Earth.

'I don't mean to sound cruel, or heartless here, but cruelty and heartlessness have been a feature in many people's lives. There has been a pervading poverty, not just in living standards, or wealth, or opportunity, but in spiritual belief. God has been all but forgotten in the rush to accumulate and speculate. The Source of the riches that have been speculated and accumulated has been cast aside in the rush and yet, and yet, that healing, Loving, energy has never been withdrawn. Spirit has continued to find light-streams to follow through the clouds of despair that man himself has created to offer hope and, for want of a better word, salvation.

'A light stream, beloved one, that surrounds you and your family now. Fear not you are not being abandoned by Spirit by embracing science, the imperative to find a vaccine has love within it. As with every garden that needs pruning you only cut back what you need to allow the new shoots space and light to blossom and you, and those like you, are new shoots however great your chronological age. Be of good heart beloved one, the gardener of this planet loves their garden and all that grows upon it with a depth of Love that is unimaginable. Shalom.'

Wardrobe doors

Dorothy: 'Shalom to you. I have just realised that before coming to speak with you, I have sent my final pieces of work to the people managing the spiritual Group that I was a member of for over thirty years. Work that I initiated so was not expected, or even wanted, but I needed to complete the process before speaking with you today. As soon as I pressed the send button I felt a sense of freedom, release, and sadness.'

Librarian: 'Ah, I thought I had lost you this morning to self-doubt and sadness.'

Dorothy: 'Indeed, you nearly did, for I felt uncomfortable about what I was hearing earlier and so deleted it and thought I would not continue today.'

Librarian: 'What does it say in the introduction about no censorship?'

Dorothy: 'I know, which is why I am back now, but what happens if I am uncomfortable about not continuing, for fear of making things up, or uncomfortable because I fear censoring you. I am dammed if I do and dammed if I don't.'

Librarian: 'Ah and there we have the crux, do we not? You fear judgement by those charged with the management of the work you have done and yet, you feared even more greatly being found wanting by your soul for not doing the work in the first place. Work you felt inspired to do and which in your heart honoured the Teachers who you love so deeply. Work that is precious to you and dare to hope it might be precious to others. So, you were dammed either way and should you have left this conversation unfinished this morning dammed there too.'

Dorothy: 'That's about right. Pressing the send button on that work and the message of explanation felt like an act of hopelessness, there is little or no chance it will be used and the intention behind it will fail. So much has been lost, so much, it is heartbreaking and I feel I was just piling another layer of beauty, care, and commitment into a wardrobe for the door to be closed on that too.'

Librarian: 'You are not alone in your feelings of despair, the wardrobe, as you put it, is indeed full. Full of hopes and dreams and plans. Plans that were so carefully laid down, words that were so carefully prepared and transmitted into life, ream upon ream of good intentions that have fallen by the wayside.

'But I will tell you this beloved one, there is no wardrobe door that can contain the Light. No man made obstruction that can stand between the Light and its purpose and every time something happens to open that wardrobe door it spills out. Every time you, your partner, and any other Group member opens their heart then the Light pours out, for the wardrobe is your collective hearts and cannot be constrained by one or two members, whatever their titles may be.

'There is nothing you have sent this morning that your soul has not retained. There is no molecule of Light that has been absorbed by yourself and your travelling companions that is not ready for action, regardless of where you are in the world or what you think your status might be. The readiness for action lies within your hearts and needs no permission other than your own.

'It is right that you honoured your Teachers for they brought us together and as I bow my head to them, they bow their head to you for following the spiritual Law with such a strong but gentle heart. Loss is your portal, more than any other, for that is the story of your childhood and it prepared you to be able to let go and move on because you have always had to let go and move on.

'Although I know that accepting the failure of the Group was painful for you and took a considerable time to heal, at no point did you let go of the Source — and neither did the Source let go of you. So, this morning as you related to, and honoured, that structure, for what may be the last time, you freed yourself to follow the Source wherever it leads you. And here's one thing I can promise you ... your end destination is not another wardrobe.'

Dorothy: *Laughing.* 'Thank goodness for that I am claustrophobic!'

Librarian: *Laughs.* 'Well you are in good company beloved one I can promise you that. Have I met your expectations this morning?'

Dorothy: 'Absolutely, thank you, I am glad I returned.'

Librarian: 'So am I and so are your Teachers who are nodding sagely as we speak. Shalom to you this day, please rest.'

Past life memory

Librarian: 'Shalom to you this day a little bruised by life I feel.'

Dorothy: 'Indeed, aching from the vaccination and from letting go of expectations that things would ever change in one area of my life. Weary, I think would best describe me today.'

Librarian: 'Expectations are a prison, are they not? They can only be created through your own life experience. You can never truly stand in the shoes of another, or understand their inner struggles, and so expectations lead to disappointment more surely than a grey day threatens rain.

'But what of hope, of stepping out of your old shoes and into new ones? Or, better still, walking barefoot on your earth, feeling its power and its grace and ability to regenerate itself. How does it do that? Well, the most obvious reason is that it does not doubt that it can. It does not nurture feelings of any kind that could prevent its re-growth, it takes the opportunities afforded to it and creates ones where it needs to. It absorbs the nutrients and life force that is around it and gives back what it came to be, be that flower, or tree or grassland. Not only that, but it invites life and should it need to adapt its behaviour to survive it does that too.

'The mind is like this, if it is encouraged and trusted. You can, and you do, follow it down well trodden pathways and then find yourself at a crossroads, or entering new terrain that was unexpected. Do you stop and retreat for safety, or do you keep exploring, perhaps leaving a trail back home? Do you give new images and ideas time to percolate, free of expectations, and invite your feelings to follow rather than lead and limit?

'Of course you do otherwise we would not be speaking, but the deeper the tracks the greater the potential for limitation. Your feelings settle and your expectations flicker once again and that can hide a fear of going deeper, surrendering once more to the unknown and following the Light.'

Dorothy: 'I understand, so I am going to pause now and see what happens ...

'I had a sense of movement and colours and now I am standing in a huge, circular marble or stone hall, with a domed roof and arched doors, it is empty, voices echo all around but I cannot see anyone. There are windows in the dome and beams of sunlight fall into the centre. There is something Egyptian about this space, it has been built to reflect the planets, stars, and Equinoxes and I feel

113

very at home. I am waiting to meet someone and I have scrolls under my arm, I am called to one of the arches where there is a small alcove where a man is sitting.

'He is clearly important, not only from the way he is dressed but the number of armed men around him, whom he waves away. There is a table which he is seated at and a stoneware jar of water which he pours into goblets, one for me and one for him. He is smiling and we are very much at ease in each other's company, we have work to do and we settle down to look at the scrolls. It could be any business meeting anywhere except for the beautiful surroundings, the cool building in the midst of such heat, but the focus is the same, but there is such love and trust there. It is really pleasant.'

Librarian: 'There are times are there not when past lives have meaning and this one of them. You know, that you have seen a snapshot of a past life with one of your Teachers. An important man in that life who relied on you and your work, but also loved you for your loyalty and your intelligence.

'That rapport and that mutual appreciation exists today and as you handed over the last of your work once again in this life, he loved you and thanked you. He also wants you to know that the completion of one project only leaves space for the next.

'Imagine you are together in that building and walking together in the cool hallways, your work completed for the day, laughing at your successes and discussing your failures and unmet expectations. From time to time, you place an arm around each other's shoulder as you recount together the road you have travelled this far. Such bon homie.

'As you move into the centre of the hall your companion points up and allows the sun to warm his face for a moment. Then he smiles as his guard approaches to remind him he is due elsewhere, he puts his hand on your shoulder and bids you rest, for there is more to do and he cannot do it without you. You smile and nod as he departs, and you leave fulfilled but ready for more.'

Dorothy: 'Thank you, that was lovely. Shalom.'

In service of God

Librarian: 'Shalom to you this day, an empty page like so many before waiting to be filled with the Light of Spirit and the machinations of the world. A day, a period of time dictated by the orbit of your planet and by the cycles of nature which provide mankind with a rhythm to their lives and change, death, renewal, and wonder. Ah! That mankind still felt wonder, for so much is now being replicated on screens that real life has become less of an experience and more of a commercial commodity.

'But, there are always two sides to a coin, and your white screen waits every morning with anticipation for what might fill it. What I might, with my infinite source of knowledge, pull off these shelves and open before you. Your fingers always poised to capture the droplets of Light that fall as words, images, impressions which you carefully record without interpretation. I sense no need in you this morning, just space and curiosity, am I right?'

Dorothy: 'Yes you are and good morning to you. May I say that feeling empty is not particularly pleasant.'

Librarian: *Laughs.* 'They say do they not, "as above so below", and that is true. But it would be more accurate, although more clumsy, to say, "as above so inverted down below", for your emptiness is my delight, just as my black is your white. Although that statement is not as elegant as the original, it does point to the possibilities that exist beyond your freewill, where your soul soars unencumbered by the concerns of the day. So, you may ask if your soul is a helium balloon released from its string, where would it travel to?'

Dorothy: 'I cannot really answer that for my imagination is limited to what I know and I don't know much about life in the Spirit realm. I suppose if I were to guess, I imagine my soul might seek answers to earthly problems.'

Librarian: 'Well you are right in a way, but like prayers, what the soul seeks out is not confined to your life, or even your families' life, but to life itself and its continuation. The fundamental conversation that the soul has with its Higher Self, and that that Higher Self has with the collective Soul, is, "what can I do to help?" On the Earth, that same question is usually, "what can you do to help me?"

'So when someone like yourself comes empty to this place that is a joy because then we can address that question together. "What can you do to help?"

'I hear your questions; who would I ask that of, and where would I send the help anyway? Although I know you know some of the answers, let us explore that a little shall we? You are asking God how you can place your energy and will to Its purpose, how you can direct your hands, feet, and heart to the outworking of the Plan and the purpose of humanity. Such a grand answer I know but you may be surprised at how a little energy can magnify in Love.

'Then you wonder where to send that help and that, surprisingly, is something you don't need to know the answer to, for the answer is to God for It and Its emissaries to distribute. The Truth is you can never know where healing or Light is most needed in your world.

'If you see your morning meditations like a stone dropped into a pool creating concentric circles of colour and Light, then your own consciousness can place certain needs in say the first one or two. But that Light and the colour, enhanced by your colours, flows where it is most needed, for it has its own God-given intelligence.

'So you see placing yourself in service of God is simple in one way, although very difficult in another, for it requires an emptiness that has been wrought from difficulty and lined with intention. It requires the removal of blinkers and the ability to open your eyes to the Light and a heart that knows it is beating to another drum beyond the cacophony of this world.

'And what does this service look like? It looks like dust motes in the sunlight. What does it sound like? The sound of the eternal Aum. How does it manifest? As droplets of hope captured by open hearts reaching out for succour — perhaps through reading words tapped out on an empty white screen in the early morning light.

'So I am grateful for your emptiness, an emptiness that was filled with Light and which prevented none of it from manifesting in your world and in service of God. Shalom to you this day, shalom.'

Dorothy: 'Shalom.'

The mirror on the horizon

Librarian: 'Shalom to you this day. Before we start, I would like you to come on a journey with me, so close your eyes and breathe. Feel the movements of the planet in your body, the magnetism, and the layers of earth beneath your feet. Sense the history within the crust of your earth, the peace just under the surface interrupted by the vibrations of life, machinery, transport, but fundamentally still, secure, safe.

'Travel in your mind's eye through the corridors created by animals, myriad tracks within the rocks that criss-cross your planet deep within the crust. See the crystal matrix, broken here and there by mining, the channels dug to extract oil and other valuable resources. And all of this before you meet the molten core, crystalline in nature, but terrifying in fact.

'Imagine in centuries gone by people living within the earth, caves being home to people and animals. All the tunnels deep under the earth hiding secrets, or made by extracting the earth for building monuments, monuments to the gods that created such a garden and provided so much. Gods that were feared and revered in equal measure. Imagine being able to walk through fertile, natural, land to rivers and seas that sparkled in the sunlight, clean, clear water perhaps filled with fish.

'Now, become aware of your apparel. Simple, animal skins, bare feet and yes, a spear at your side. But listen to your heart it is steady and still, alert yes, but fearful? No. There is a sense of wonder, is there not? A sense of space and belonging not to someone, or something, but to the earth itself. A feeling of delight as you anticipate meeting another person, your curiosity about them and their lives and their family. It's calming and reassuring, is it not?'

Dorothy: 'Yes it is, strangely yes it is, for I would imagine there were dangers too and rivalry?'

Librarian: 'Yes there were and make no mistake life was a struggle a lot of the time. As acquisition grew, so the turf wars increased, but there was a fundamental difference that I want you to experience and that is that sense of belonging. Reconnect to that feeling now, of being one with the earth, with the landscape, with everything that lived around you.

'It is that experience, as natural as breathing at that time, that led to acceptance. The acceptance I was hoping to demonstrate is the acceptance of wonder, of awe, of being part of something so great it was beyond imagination. It just was and you just were, who you were unencumbered by judgement or comparison, a free human being in a beautiful garden. There is a sense of peace is there not, a feeling of being loved?

'So why have I chosen this imagery this morning? A strange choice you might think in your sophisticated and mechanised world. It is to demonstrate two things; firstly what it feels like to be a soul in the Spirit realm, that depth of acceptance interlaced with wonder and awe, and secondly the lesson humanity is facing at this time. For the pandemic has brought with it a stillness, a quietness, and an awakening within, balancing a life that has become too complicated, too removed from what matters and the rhythms of life. Where wealth has led to great poverty and inequality.

'Now, I am not proposing the wholesale demolition of all your buildings and a return to cave dwelling, not at all, but I am pointing to the fact that acceptance and belonging are easier when living a more natural life. That acceptance comes like a cool balm when people live in harmony with nature, for everything else follows on naturally and the generations flourish together.

'At the moment people fear having their wings clipped, so to speak, being forced to stay close to home and unable to travel to foreign climes. But at the same time they are rediscovering their homes and their neighbourhoods and understanding where they belong. Not on virtual platforms, but on the streets where they live and with the neighbours that they have needed to rely on. They have experienced for themselves the importance of family, the stress of being separated by continents, unable to fly to a bedside or hold the hand of a loved one who is dying.

'Out of all this so many will accept that life cannot return to what it was. Not because it cannot return but because it should not return, it was unnatural and unhealthy and separated people and families from one another. It was false freedom for it imprisoned people for years in jobs that drained their life force in the pursuit of a future that often never came.

'It will not need governments to dictate these changes, for as the energy of the earth rises in humanity so humanity will rise in the people of this earth. As humanity rises, they will rediscover their wonder and who they truly are and what they belong to, and peace will take its chance and fill every heart. This is my prayer, for humanity holds its future in its hands and the pandemic has painted a mirror on every horizon. Do not close your eyes beloved one, love what you see for you are seeing Love itself. So be it and shalom.'

The gift

Librarian: 'Shalom to you this day. A day that has already contained meditation and an image that fascinates you am I right?'

Dorothy: 'Shalom and yes, you are. The image I saw was just a glimpse of a white figure, high up in the distance, female, I think. She was standing in an arched building and was rather like a High Priestess. The image is becoming clearer as I try to recall it, she has blond hair and kind blue eyes and is beckoning me to go and sit with her as she walks down the steps from her dais. We go and sit in one of the arches and she hands me something, placing her hands over mine as I take it and putting her finger to her lips as if this is a secret. She then gets up and leaves me holding this small box.

'It is wooden with gold inlay, lined with gold silk and … I think it is empty. I keep trying to imagine what it might contain but however much I try to put a form around it, it simply contains Light, a droplet of Light like a teardrop. When I open the lid this teardrop hangs mysteriously in thin air. It is charming for it is like petrol on water, all the colours on a translucent background. As I imagine it I can see it hovering above my palm so it is not confined to the box.'

Librarian: 'Indeed it is not confined to the box, or to anything else, it is a gift, a gift of Light that has within it the essence of femininity and strength. The image of the High Priestess is one of a bridge between your world and the world of Spirit. She stood high up to represent her role as a bridge, but came down to meet you when she saw you were ready. She was kindly and gentle, but wanted you to know that this is a gift to treasure. Not to lock away in a box but to free it from the container and place it in your heart.

'It particularly resonates to your palm chakras, to healing, which is why you could see it spinning over your palm chakra. It is an image that I know will never leave you, for its mere existence has an effect does it not?'

Dorothy: 'Yes it does, I am tempted to say that it seems to both draw in energy and give our energy.'

Librarian: 'It does, it is intelligent, it assesses your need and will assess the needs of others and then spins to provide what is needed. In truth the Christos Light needs no symbols, but there are times on anyone's journey when a gift is a recognition of progress, and this was indeed a gift.'

Dorothy: 'I am very moved and honoured. Thank you.'

Librarian: 'Beloved one it has been earned and the meaning will become clearer in time. Do not stress over the imagery, or try to recreate the moment, the gift has been accepted into your heart and there it will be nurtured and grow.

'It is an emotional moment for me too, I feel such pride that such a gift can be accepted so easily. So, often gifts fall by the wayside, the intended recipients are disappointed or blind to their arrival, or their personality rejects the opening to Soul that needs to take place to allow the transmission. But no, you glimpsed something and did not dismiss it and in not arguing with it or yourself you could allow it to settle in your heart and to feel its benefit.'

Dorothy: 'I too feel emotional, as if my heart is expanding in my chest. I feel I need to sit quietly now and allow the whole experience to settle, so thank you.'

Librarian: 'My Love surrounds you as you sit in peace. Fear not beloved one a gift once given cannot be withdrawn. Shalom.'

The soul in life

Dorothy: 'Shalom.'

Librarian: 'Shalom to you this day and to the peace that fills you, it is quite palpable even in your world it is like spring sunlight on new shoots rising from the cold earth. It illuminates who you are and opens up possibilities. Where shall we go today? What shall I pull off my dusty shelves and open before you? What do you need?'

Dorothy: 'I don't feel any need except perhaps a desire not to leave with an empty page because this time is precious. I would like to share the fact that I can instantly recall the spinning teardrop of colour and feel the warmth in my palm chakra when I do. As I waited for you to speak I imagined different colours spinning out, blue and then pink and then saw a lit passageway before me.'

Librarian: 'Every day you say, "I believe in the Light," and this is a demonstration, is it not, of what that belief means, for within that Light is everything you need to progress and indeed for mankind to progress.

'At every stage there are corridors of learning shall we say, passageways or bridges, that need to be traversed so you can progress. You cannot ski off-piste if you have never encountered the nursery slopes, and spiritual progress mirrors this in numerous ways.

'First you must choose your landscape with care and your teachers and companions too. Your progress can be hindered by mockery, or competition or an impatient tutor. Although the real lesson is self-confidence and courage in the early days it is often clouded by technique, technical terms and instructions that fill your head and sap your confidence to even stand up straight. Pleasure and freedom, shall we say, are far from your thoughts as you stare at your misbehaving feet.

'Then with perseverance you master the technique and the vocabulary and begin to focus on your core, who you are and why you came to the mountain. One day, you pause and realise that there is so much that is unexplored within this landscape and beyond. So much more this landscape has to offer, not just in your mastery of it, but its connection with you, its ability to heal and inspire and bring peace and your focus changes.

'You take the ski lift to the summit, quite alone now, and stand awhile aware that there are so many possibilities, so many routes as yet undiscovered. You notice the snow glinting in one part and inviting your presence, and so you move off with a confidence in yourself and in the light that is pointing the way forward. That is not serendipity, that is how your belief in the Light manifests — in pointing your way forward, passageways that you have opened up through technical knowledge, self-control, and courage and, your old friend, tenacity.

'So image that passageway again and tell me what you see.'

Dorothy: 'I'm not really seeing anything, although I feel bathed in a soft gold and green that seems to be settling on my skin.'

Librarian: 'Well I would call that something would you not? How do you feel?'

Dorothy: 'Completely peaceful, there is a sense of everything moving into a vortex at my solar plexus as if all the systems of my body have harmonised one with another. A total healing, leaving me feeling a little light-headed.'

Librarian: 'Passageways in Spirit are not corridors in life, they are movements in vibration that you move through, or to be more accurate, that move through you opening your mind and your perceptions that little bit more. Always gentle and carefully calibrated by your Teachers and your soul to enhance your progress and increase your confidence.

'Many people would dismiss the experiences you have had these last two days as uneventful, even disappointing, after all no great revelations to report, no conversations with alien beings, just an empty box and a passageway that led nowhere. But that's the point is it not? If your soul is within every cell of your body then its expansion into life will be felt in the cells of your being and that expansion will be initiated by the ingress of Light. For what is spiritual progress if it is not the expansion of your soul into life?

'Treasure these experiences, I know they are unforgettable, but give them your trust too for they are the gateways people spend lifetimes searching for and passing by. Enjoy your day, my love surrounds you, shalom.'

Dorothy: 'Shalom and thank you.'

Vapour trails

Librarian: 'Beloved one good morning to you and shalom. In such a short time we have become companions have we not, companions on passageways that have no visible depth to them but which orient you towards new perspectives to your life. A life that I know feels constrained and different to the rest of your days on this beautiful planet of yours.

'A difference that has led you here and given you the time to stay awhile, to get comfortable in the old armchair and to listen to words that have no sound but much meaning. Words that end when your heart is full of Light and not before. So, what shall we speak on today?'

Dorothy: 'Good morning, my agenda is always the same to see what emerges. But is that too passive? Does that leave all the work up to you?'

Librarian: *Laughs.* 'Do not worry on that score, beloved one. I am delighted that a soul in life has the time to stop by for a chat one, who is curious enough about the Realm I inhabit to clear their mind of constructs and to listen and wait. For you see I marvel at my world even though I have never known anything else, for it is constantly changing. As life on earth changes so do the energetic replicas that emerge all over this Realm. As the freewill of mankind creates problems so the Halls of Learning take on new subjects, new avenues of exploration, not to discover what is going on, that is already known, but to explore the means of effective intervention.

'Imagine if you will virtual cities appearing all the time; universities and laboratories, schools and churches all created in the image of what has been constructed before, all full of people intent on working collaboratively on the current problems. The dynasties of the past all represented in holographic form and the different disciplines all focussed on one thing: helping humanity.

'You see absolute knowledge has limited benefit if there are no means of communicating it to those most in need. Love is not enough if it is not experienced as a living energy, and Soul is impotent in the face of denial. I think one of your Teachers once described us as, "an army waiting for the resources to be able to act," a perfect description in my opinion.

'Now I know that you think of yourself as empty and open as you arrive here and that is partly true and much appreciated, but you are like an aeroplane that leaves a vapour trail as you make your journey. Firstly, rather like our passageway that went nowhere yesterday, your journey is entirely internal and happens over time, you first felt my signal during your early meditation, then I stayed during breakfast, and now you feel you have arrived. That has left a vapour trail, but in this case, it is not disbursing waste products it is disbursing Light, and it is two-way, our consciousness' have been entwined during that period.

'This vapour trail is not linear it is a spiral that magnifies as it enters your world and here, may I say, it is the purity of Light that I am able to connect to that is distributed. Now that is very important for you to understand, the purity of the Light Source affects its ability to travel. If it is permitted to enter your world through conduits such as yourself then Masters and Teachers manage that transmission, they give their blessing so to speak.

'There are other, less refined, energies affecting your world, all the time, of course there are, and if they find conduits then they transmit too, but the transmission is more limited, more person to person than collective. Although those transmissions can provide useful learning too.

'Your "arrival" here creates a spiral of Light, one that spins as we speak and distributes not just the Light that is generated, but the shared knowledge, for your concerns and questions have universal applications. How many people out there are concerned about the same things that you are? Millions, I would guess. So, these conversations enable the purity of spiritual Light to entwine with the consciousness of mankind. Making it more potent and usable by others who may have an idea, or a thought, millions of miles from you, but no distance at all from me. Should you feel relief, for example, that relief spreads, you see this happen with hatred and fear so why not in Love and peace?'

Dorothy: 'Why not indeed?'

Librarian: 'So do you see why there is nothing passive about these encounters? True spiritual engagement can never be personal, it is always collective and very precious to those of us in Spirit privileged enough to speak to a soul in life? The future of mankind quite literally depends on these vapour trails, there can never be too many, there can only be too few. So, as your skies clear of aeroplanes pray that others, like you, have turned inward and upward so that your skies clear of the clouds of distrust and despair, for they are the true polluters of your world.

'Thank you for your visit beloved one, shalom.'

Dorothy: 'Shalom and thank you, such wonderful imagery.'

Librarian: 'The Light is mine, but the palette is yours beloved one, thank you for letting me paint with it.'

Thought patterns

Librarian: 'Beloved one shalom to you this day. I know you are keen to share your nighttime experiences with me, and so I will listen with interest.'

Dorothy: 'Thank you and good morning. Indeed, I think you are I were in dialogue around 1am.'

Librarian: 'Well I can confirm the dialogue, beloved one, but not the time having no watch.'

'*Laughs.* 'I think you are curious about whether you interrupted a dream conversation between myself and your soul by waking up am I right?'

Dorothy: 'Yes you are.'

Librarian: 'In that case I can confirm that a dialogue between your soul and myself was joined at one point by yourself and it was a pleasure. It turned a line into a triangle as you stayed awhile. That was pleasing because, as you are aware, conversations such as the one I was having with your soul, while you were sleeping, are not uncommon, it is the main form of spiritual communication with all souls in life. A golden thread always connects the soul and the body and during the night should the personality wake up from sleep the soul snaps back into the body.

'However, on this occasion, and on others, you visited, stayed and joined in, so that was a pleasure. I do hope it was edifying? Before you continue, may I reassure you that, should we be interrupted this morning, I will return at our usual appointed time. Or, to be more accurate, I will still be available when you return and have a quiet moment to conclude our discussions. As must be obvious by now you are welcome any time, your armchair is empty and your tea brews gently by its side.'

Dorothy: *Laughs.* 'Thank you. It was indeed edifying and rather humbling to think of all the times I asked my Teachers what I could do, how I needed to change to follow the Teachings. How keen I was to meet their expectations rather, like the frightened girl I was as a child.

'What the last few days have illustrated is how the spiritual path is entirely internal. Every step is some realisation, some cleansing from life, be it this one or a past life, in order to accept yourself entirely as a child of God. How amazing simple it is, it is about being, not doing. It is about stillness, not movement. It is about openness, not defensiveness, and it's about self Love and acceptance first and foremost.

'How astonishingly simple and blindingly obvious it seems now. Yet, how complicated life makes it. My misinterpretation of spiritual Teachings took me on many journeys, which, I thought, were designed to enrobe me with knowledge, but in fact the opposite turned out to be true. I thought that my acceptance suggested specialness, but I now realise that the purpose of the guided journey was to return me to what I am: a child of God, like everyone else.

'All of this illustrated in two images; a gift box that seemed to contain nothing and a passageway without depth, but which I merged with and moved forward in by standing still.'

Librarian: 'Well there you have it and in your descriptions and their effect on you we see the power of thought alone, do we not? Two simple images that can change everything ... let us continue later, but I am glad you at least captured your nighttime thoughts without interruption.'

...

Dorothy: 'Shalom once again. I am nervous about this because in our earlier meditation I was reminded of a situation which was so painful it brought tears to my eyes and tightened my solar plexus. I don't know how easy it is going to be for me to open to you because I still feel the emotion of that occurrence.'

Librarian: 'I am aware of the memory that arose unbidden from the imagery your partner was using. But it was not entirely serendipitous, for we were speaking earlier about the power of thought, were we not? But in that context it was the power of positive or creative thought.

'The experience that you remembered was the result of negative thoughts and feelings that governed the actions of another. Fear took hold and was misdirected towards your presence because he was struggling with the demands of his role at that time.

'However, what was heartening for me to see was that the instant you remembered the slight, and the subsequent denials, you remembered the kindness of others who leapt to reassure you and to restore your place. You had been invited and it was to your credit that you stayed.

'As much as his action, possibly unconscious, affected you then, what continues to affect you now, years later, are your own thoughts about it. You still do not accept that it might have been accidental, as claimed, and it is these thoughts that continue to feed the negativity. Only you can let them go, only you can seek self-forgiveness for the negativity that existed within the relationship that led to that unthinking act. Only you can own your fragility, for you were after all attending a meeting, where the agenda was itself dissolution, aware that you were being relegated to the outer reaches of the work.

'The removal of your place was a foretaste of what you were about to suffer, it was not the instigator of it, your soul was and I know you find that hard to bear but no longer impossible to accept. Those that stood by you then stand by you now and what has blossomed would not have bloomed in quite the same way if you had not followed your soul in the way that you have.

'I do not seek to minimise your heartbreak that day and subsequently, not at all, but to point to the fact that thought patterns exist only if energised. If you remove your energy from them, you release yourself from maintaining a belief that is no longer useful to you.

Dorothy: 'That's very helpful, thank you.'

Librarian: 'I would also remind you that you did not suffer alone that day, your Teachers were also heartbroken so you were in good company and they never left your side as you did not leave theirs.

'So worth returning after all? Until tomorrow beloved one, until tomorrow I will set my alarm clock.'

Fear & courage

I was thinking about fear
and how it weights your soul,
and wondered if it could prevent
you reaching your life's goals?

I hear a distant answer,
that fear's a lesson too,
it exists to keep you safe,
but not your being to imbue.

It can become a blanket
that keeps you from all harm,
but equally it can become
an agent of great charm.

It can disconnect your courage,
which everybody needs,
for courage is the staff of life,
if you are to succeed.

You need courage to face karma,
and to act with quiet resolve,
when you encounter problems,
that you alone can solve.

You need courage to look upwards,
to reach beyond your field of vision,
and courage to look inwards
to fulfil your soul's ambition.

Change

Librarian: 'Beloved one and so you arrive once more, what a pleasure. This time you are already primed, shall we say, with images of seas and oceans hosting sleeping typhoons and hurricanes, forces more powerful than any who can speak to mankind through mediums. Forces that remind man of the power of Creation and their place within it.

'But what of the hurricanes within the hearts of man? Those awakened by rhetoric and fear, where impassioned individuals who feel downtrodden or ignored take to the streets with weapons and rage? Where lives are lost and differences laid bare, what of these forces of nature should they be encouraged to ensure that man is free?

'The passion in the heart of men and women is a gift and that gift, perhaps more than any other, needs to be interlaced with Love. For it is through Love that passion can embrace difference and be harnessed towards the outworking of the Plan of the Creation. It needs passion to stop the destruction of your world and to implore people to change their ways and to find what unites them in this task. It takes passion to open people's hearts and minds to the needs of others, especially those who are silent and feel oppressed. But passion alone can become a blunt force and can itself become the oppressor.

'So I choose my words carefully, do I not? Interlaced with Love, for then the passion of one does not become a stick with which to beat another. It does not seek to destroy its opposition, but to find the common ground and build on that together.

'No hurricane destroys only what has outgrown its usefulness, no pandemic affects only those who are ready to return, and no victor takes control of a vibrant city or population. So better, surely, to seek out the common passions, the armature of peace that has served people well enough until now and build on that. Love becomes interlaced through the seeking and the curiosity and listening that it awakens to form a bond that ignites the passion in all and ensures greater success.

'Better then to understand the passions of others as well as to harness the passions of the self and to place both in the service of Love.'

Dorothy: 'Amazing, thank you. As you were speaking I was seeing images of the destroyed cities in Iraq, cities now just rubble, a few people darting between the ruins trying to live there still, shell shocked and frightened. The women

129

appearing as black shadows against the sandy ruins. I tried to image the city as it once was with markets, gardens, trees, courtyards, houses, and children playing in the streets, but it was impossible to see how anything could be done now except to sweep it all away. All that history is now just rubble.'

Librarian: 'And who is the victor? Where is the freedom to be found? Not on the streets or in the bombed out cities, or in the refugee camps, or on the streets of strange countries where the lucky have fled, or even in the seas where their brothers and sisters have drowned?

'But do you know where freedom is the most absent? In the hearts of all the citizens of that country, wherever they may be and whichever side they favoured. War imprisons hearts for it places a cage around them not just for one generation, but for many. It creates a deep-seated sense of impermanence that can be impervious to Love and peace as it continues to protect the heart from a perceived threat that may have vanished long ago.

'Please do not misunderstand me, I am not saying that nothing must change in the world, a great deal must change, but it is how that change is enacted that is important to its success. The impassioned changes that are needed at this time demand that what is best within mankind comes to the fore. That the love in their hearts is set free and their souls are welcomed into the garden of life which is their home. No finger pointing, banner waving or baseball bat will be required, indeed you might be hard-pressed to hear a murmur as the quiet revolution sweeps your streets like thieves in the night.'

Dorothy: 'Beautiful, thank you.'

Librarian: 'Shalom and peace be with you as I know you are dealing with some destruction of your own.'

A walk in the forest

Librarian: 'Beloved one take my hand and walk with me awhile. Can you hear the birdsong, can you feel the grass beneath your feet and the sun on your face? This forest is one I love, it is birchwood and pine and the scent of the pine lifts my spirits and the mottled trunks paint pictures as I walk. Shade and light flicker and small animals rustle all around us feeling our presence, for we are silent as we walk through their world. Invisible to mankind but visible to them as moving shadows that bear the possibility of threat, so they run and hide and then relax as we walk on.

'The pines are ancient, dark, and mysterious and too grand to react to our presence, they give of their scent freely as we pass by. There it is, I sense a tension in you, alert to being stalked perhaps by some creature of the forest. But remember you are invisible to them and bear no scent of your own, so they go about their business raising their young and basking in the sunlight. How does it feel to be invisible in your natural world?'

Dorothy: 'Rather lovely in fact. I can imagine being out in nature and no threat at all to the animals that live there, even wild ones. I did have a sense of being stalked but it was more a sense of the movement and motion of the body that I reacted to, I was not afraid.'

Librarian: 'The point of this exercise, if exercise it is, is to point to the nature of personhood. How, if you do not tune your senses, you become encased in a cloak that not only protects you from inclement weather but also from the movements of life around you.

'I know you love the sea and often comment that you don't want to be in it or on it but beside it, watching, its presence alone washing any stress from you as surely as a warm bath. That is because it is near the sea that the movements of the earth are magnified. No one can sit or walk by the sea and not be affected, it is as if the pores of their skin open up be it to storm or placid waves. Their physical form expands to include their environment and the creatures that they share it with.

'But the forests speak another language, they speak of timelessness, of history and of stability. The trees speak of healing and peace and safety and you imagine journeys through a forest to a clearing, moving out of the darkness into the light and out of constriction into an expanse of possibilities.

'Just two aspects of your natural world that offer so much to humanity. What a mind it took to create such gifts from thought alone, to anticipate the needs of men and women for succour and well being. To realise that a garden would be needed not only to provide food and shelter, but to nurture their souls by bringing peace in their wake.

'What Love is entwined within those thoughts, what care, like a family expecting a child preparing the ground for their growth and well being long before the due date, preparing themselves for parenthood and yes, grandparents for grandparenthood.

'Such exquisite beauty conceived by thought alone. A creative process like no other for there was no past to provide a blueprint, just the needs of the Soul for experience as the guiding Light and a total absence of fear because the imperative was Love.

'It is breathtaking, is it not?'

Dorothy: 'Yes it is, it leaves me speechless to be honest because it is quite simply beyond my imagination, so I do not try to explain it even to myself.'

Librarian: 'I believe your partner's inspirer talked about the value of leaving the mysterious mysterious recently, and with this I concur entirely. It is a mystery and it is magnificent and, from my perspective, far safer outside of the intelligent reach of mankind. But as you touch the trunks of your great trees, or shelter under their leaves, or watch the tides ebb and flow allow yourself to feel that mystery. To feel awe and gratitude for it is that that opens you up to the movements of the planets and the place of Soul within the universe.

'Shalom to you this day, shalom.'

Finding the Source

Librarian: 'Shalom beloved one and I feel your emotions before you even speak, so tell me what bothers you.'

Dorothy: 'Shalom to you and thank you. When I started the early morning meditation I wondered how I could ask you a question without causing offence and then my partner's channelling echoed that, hence the emotion.

'His inspirer indicated a change in his importance as a Guide in our lives. Now I know he was being encouraging and affirming about our development, but nonetheless I feel a great stab of loss mixed with gratitude and love. I know he is not stepping back, or away, but it is still a shift and one that puts me in mind of my debt to him. I simply do not think I would have survived the most painful years of my life without his presence and I have done my best to follow his advice and take it to my heart. I hope he knows how grateful I am and how deeply I love him.'

Librarian: 'My beloved one he knows, he knows, and he has relied on you too and has not been disappointed. No successful relationship between Spirit and mankind is ever in one direction, it cannot be, for it emerges and develops out of shared Love and need. Both need each other to fulfil their purpose and there is gratitude on both sides.

'This I believe takes us into the territory that you feel might cause offence for is it not linked? Before you speak let me sit myself down and take a sip of tea, I have never been offended before so this will be a new experience for me.'

Dorothy: *Laughing.* 'I know, but being concerned about the effect my words may have is a good thing, is it not?'

Librarian: 'In normal circumstances yes it is a good thing and choosing your words carefully when speaking with Spirit is helpful too. But remember your question is written in neon in your aura so I know it already and was carefully considering my response before you even sat down. You see your soul and I always have a little dialogue about the real questions behind your carefully phrased questions.'

Dorothy: 'Well in that case I'll be brief. I was musing on the value of our conversations, more for you than for me. Or, to put it another way, why would you spend time with someone of my age when surely speaking to someone much younger would have a greater impact on them and on life in general?'

Librarian: *Laughs.* 'Well it appears I am not the only one answering your question this morning. You have already been told, have you not, that because you are both so familiar with the Source you no longer need to rely upon a Guide?'

Dorothy: 'Yes, that's right.'

Librarian: 'Then it would be cruel, would it not, for the Source to be unresponsive to the arrival of one of Its children? Surely all the religions and faiths, all the wars and the attempts at suppression and dominance have had a fragment of meaning or Truth within them, a signpost, however misguided, to something greater, towards home?

'Those of us in Spirit who are charged with guiding humanity have infinite patience, if you had not spoken with me in this life I would have waited to speak to the next Aspect of your soul that incarnates. I have many, many charges and each one is so important to me because each one that bears the Light into life helps me to fulfil my purpose; which is to help all of humanity to achieve theirs.

'So nothing is a waste of my time, not one word, one sentence, one fragment of Light. Indeed, it is always a blessing, regardless of whether you were bedridden and about to return home or a toddler with many years ahead of you. Every lifetime is like a blink of my eye, but beloved one, every blink bears healing potential within it and together we are realising ours.

'The Source is there for all without exception. Yeshua, more than any other Teacher, demonstrated that in His life. His words live on, do they not? He lived a short life relative to yours and His period of Ministry was even shorter as he was not Christed until His baptism. He spoke simply to anyone who would listen, with the hope of igniting the same Light within them as was within Him. His mission was to point people to the Source within and he dismissed no one for all were worthy and all are worthy, but so few of them feel themselves to be so.

'So you see, no offence taken, our Love is unconditional for it cannot be otherwise. The journey you have made is one that is due respect, for more than one Guide has walked beside you, ahead of you and carried you at times. You are loved, greatly loved, as are all of humanity if only they realised it and believed it to be true. That singular statement is the portal that all those on the spiritual path seek out, and yet most walk past the door handle over and over again. The eternal Light of Yeshua lives on in and will always live on for it is the Light of Love and will never cease. Shalom to you this day, shalom.'

A parade of snails

Dorothy: 'I would like to share some imagery with you, more for fun than anything else. It all began with your humour yesterday when you spoke about taking a sip of tea ...'

Librarian: 'So it's my fault?'

Dorothy: 'Not at all. It is just that when I was awake early this morning I imagined all your charges, like myself, as holographic snails bringing their own homes with them to your Library and how you adapt to each one. A cup of tea here, a teepee there, a park bench somewhere else ...'

Librarian: *Laughing* 'What a spectacle that would be, for there is no part of your world that I do not "adapt" to, to use your word. No part of your world, or even mine, that my Light does not flow through and listen and speak to. I am as much in the wind as I am in the shanty towns, or ancient cities long since buried. In your parlance I am not even an "I" for I am an indivisible part of a collective with multiple personalities, a "we" if you like. I am like your worst possible schizophrenic breakdown.

'Why do you think you position me as a Librarian: in a library of Lives? You know that does not exist even in the Spirit realms, although it does mirror some of the reality of the Akashic records. But it does accurately reflect that a Light Being such as myself can be giving one part of life their full attention while simultaneously appearing in multiple stories at the same time. It is not just that you imagine me as the guardian of the books but as a character in many of them too, for what part of life past, present, or future does not need more Light?

'I am not placing myself as a Source of The Light, you understand, but as an illustration of how, where your imagination has a parade of characters all making their way to me accompanied by their familiar haunts, the reverse is also true. As much as souls find their way here during their incarnations, so I too travel in this Realm and in yours and bring what I can in whatever way I can. If that is whispered on a warm breeze on a sunny day, or captured in a prayer or affirmation, or resting in the eyes of a newborn child, I am satisfied. For Light is the universal language of Love, and that is what I bring and will continue to bring.

'Your imagery may well be seen as fun and quirky, but it has Truth within it too. It is true that Spirit constantly reacts to the shifts in the surrounding energy, whether that is a prayer, a visitor, like yourself, the turning of the planets or the calls of the Hierarchy. Energy just is, it cannot be divided it just is, but it is calibrated and moderated according to the spiritual development of the individual souls and Higher Selves. If it were not souls would be blinded by the Light that they are not yet ready to bear.

'This ability, nay necessity, to fluctuate and assimilate is, strangely, one of the main obstacles that defeats many on the spiritual path. They expect certainty and consistency and are disappointed when the advice they receive speaks to the moment and not a lifetime. Gentle advice that is so often misinterpreted and narrowly applied to the concerns of the moment while ignoring the bigger context entirely. It is easy to become angry with Spirit for we respond to the needs of your soul and not your personality. You have been there yourself.'

Dorothy: 'Indeed I have. Spirit take the long view and have the patience and superior knowledge to know that the right outcome will be achieved eventually. Regardless of what the personality wants.'

Librarian: 'The right outcome for the soul you mean?'

Dorothy: 'I do.'

Librarian: 'Well, as always, both is true. There is absolute consistency from Spirit to mankind when it comes to Love, Light and peace. There is one ultimate purpose which is for the collective that is Soul to be reunited with the God energy and the route to that is through adherence to Universal Law. The fluctuation and adaptation comes from the myriad ways in which that purpose could be achieved, the individuality of every spiritual path, the inclusion of karma and the timing within the Spheres. Let's use yourself as an example, you have followed many avenues associated with your spiritual progress and some have come to fruition and some have not. Now is that purely to do with timing, or was the initiative ill-conceived in some way or even ill-advised?

'There's no one answer, of course, but the experience that you gained is now coalescing into an integrated whole that has great depth within it. Each element was valuable and was supported by your spiritual Teachers, but they were part of your development not its sum total, and the collective progress was as important as your individual one. It is said I believe, "that all roads lead to Rome," and when the personality maintains its spiritual connection to the Light, the soul shines upon the earthly path, so whether you reach your destination by bicycle or limousine makes no difference. So thank you for sharing your imagery, I will enjoy creating my own parade of snails, habit intact. Shalom to you this day.'

Describing the Christos

Dorothy: 'Shalom to you this day. I am pleased to be here but don't have much to say.'

Librarian: 'Shalom. I can see the shimmer within your aura of the experience of the Christos that you have been alerted to. I chose those words carefully because the experience arises within and, although your partner's inspirer drew your attention to it and it was magnified by this, it was not entirely dependent on that. The Christos dwells within everyone but so few people are ready, as you are, to receive it, to affirm it, to trust it and to accept it fully.

'I noticed you did not "compare notes" as suggested, so perhaps you would like to reflect on that experience with me?'

Dorothy: 'I was aware that we did not speak of it and I think that was because it is too personal to speak of, even with my partner. I know this is absolutely not the case, but it is one of those experiences that you, or I, fear will jinx it, or cause it to evaporate if I mention it to others. I prefer in, say a healing session or group, to say nothing and just hope other people are feeling it. Occasionally, I have drawn attention to it after the event, so to speak, but I worry people are being polite if they agree they felt it too, or will feel inadequate if they felt nothing, a catch 22.

'I would describe the experience this morning as similar to feeling the quickening of a baby inside me. I was feeling very peaceful as he was speaking, but when he spoke about projecting the energy towards me, it was as if there was a surge of golden Light within my belly. It reminded me of being pregnant and the intensity of Love that I felt for our unborn child and to this day I feel for our two sons.'

Librarian: 'That is an interesting analogy as it points to two Truths, firstly the inherent strength within most pregnancies. When the soul has chosen incarnation then the mother's body has to accommodate that need and there is an eternal life force within that foetus that is akin to the power of the Christos. The whole birth process is intense, powerful, beautiful and moves most people to tears, even when watching the delivery of other children, or animals.

'Then you point to the fragility of the Christos, eternal, strong and beautiful, but which flowers and flourishes only when the ground is soft and yielding and prepared. It needs an open heart and the gentle hands of a gardener to nourish the seed and to bring forth growth, or else it remains in the dark soil of ignorance, unable to bring forth its shoot of Light.

'Such a magnificent Light, just searching for the words to describe it bring tears to my eyes. Perhaps this is the best description; that indescribable energy that fills you with beauty and healing and your eyes with tears. Thank you, beloved Lord, for I feel your presence within it and your abiding Love.'

Dorothy: 'This is quite a task is it not describing the indescribable?'

Librarian: *Laughs.* 'Well at least we are not on our own, I am in good company as I hope you feel yourself to be?'

Dorothy: 'Absolutely, but it's like trying to capture a rainbow, nothing can really describe the beauty, or its effect. And yet, it's something I would so love to be more commonplace so it could be shared, perhaps not as easily as discussing the weather, but in ordinary conversations between equals and friends.'

Librarian: 'Then we have to ensure, both of us, that this sharing continues, do we not? You might be surprised at how many people long to have these conversations so they could ground their experiences by sharing them. You are right at the start of the golden Age, so in time sharing will become more commonplace, the intensity will increase because, like this morning, the Christos Light will be magnified by contact with others and their inspirers. I am grateful for your sharing with me this morning, thank you.'

Dorothy: 'I suspect I could not have kept it a secret even if I'd wanted to.'

Librarian: 'True, but I would not have pried open the experience if you had said "no". Although there are no boundaries between you and me, I do respect your wishes, for who am I to judge whether you needed more time to integrate that experience before speaking about it. All of us, even me, sometimes need space to fully feel something and to let it trickle through our consciousness before cohering it into sentences which immediately limit it. That, I would suggest, is particularly true of the Christos for it holds such depth and potential within it, it is like finding your feet again after they have been washed clean in a whole, warm, ocean of Love.

'Gosh, the metaphors are flying today! Time to sign off, I suggest, or we'll have none left for tomorrow. Shalom to you this day, shalom.'

The Trinity

Librarian: 'Shalom to you. Every day I see you struggle to settle and ensure a clear connection, but, beloved one, you underestimate my strength and my desire to converse with you. Now, there is something on your mind, is there not? An image from your earlier meditation where the inspirer built on your experience of yesterday and I am keen to discuss it with you.'

Dorothy: 'Shalom, and thank you. In the earlier meditation when the inspirer was talking about the Christos arising from within and the inspired Teachings coming from beyond the self, the image that I saw was the Trinity: intelligence, Love and humanity. The Trinity that Yeshua embodied of course and which in our Teachings also echo the three aspects of God.'

Librarian: 'And there was no surprise really, was there? Just a shadow of a realisation that if it was a true armature for Spirit then it follows that it is true for mankind?'

Dorothy: 'Something like that, although any comparison with Yeshua I tend to shy away from.'

Librarian: 'Indeed I understand that and it was this that I was pointing to earlier; your tendency to demur. However, in every way I prefer to be speaking with someone who demurs a little too much than to someone who takes a grain of Truth and proclaims it as a field of wheat. So, no complaints from me.

'To answer your question though which was, I believe, "is this a true analogy," then the answer is yes. You are more than aware of, "as above so below," and this is another example, indeed an example of a foundation of life itself. If the purpose of mankind is to experience Love then the trinity is essential is it not? Without a body, they could not move around and experience the earth which was built for that very purpose. The body is essential for procreation and in order for that to be successful there has to be a vehicle for desire, need, and instinct.

'Then you have the Love element which is so often interpreted by mankind as desire and sentiment, for indeed they are expressions of it, but the driving energy of Love is beyond that and comes from within. It is nurtured, hopefully, by your family, but it is also greater than your earthly experience for you are born with it. It can be encouraged to thrive, or whither, but that innate memory of Love never leaves you and never ceases to search for an outlet. Even the cruellest prisoner cut off from life often nurtures a small bird or a mouse.

'The aspect of intelligence could easily be misinterpreted as scholarly achievement, but it is more aligned to the ability to function in the world. A person may be nonverbal or withdrawn, but the intelligence would still be present, their soul is still present, but they are not presenting in the same way as others are. What I am trying to say is it is not the outward expression that indicates intelligence but the inner journey, which was why your earlier speaker talked about intelligence, or inspiration, being reached for beyond the self.'

Dorothy: 'So often when we speak I wonder at the simplicity of these lessons and the time it has taken me to understand them, even partially.'

Librarian: 'It's like watching one of your quiz shows is it not and shouting the answers at the TV screen, so obvious to you and yet so hard to capture by the contestant. There is a simplicity to the framework of Creation that is breathtaking in its beauty, but its real beauty is in its ability to support all potentiality, its fluid strength.

'If you imagine yourself as a leaf on an enormous tree that is given the opportunity to explore its home during the summer months. You would start by detaching yourself from an outer twig, and then practically blindfolded, would have to navigate a plethora of twigs, branches and dead ends. You may be stopped in your tracks by wind or rain, but even if you find your way to the trunk you cannot possibly know it's height, or its depth, so which way do you turn?

'I don't need to conclude the metaphor except to remind you that that leaf has but one summer before it falls to earth and that is true of life. It is but a short time to unravel the complexities of life, some man made, some God given, back to the Source and to discover the beauty and symmetry that is there. Not to mention having the wit to look within you and see that symmetry replicated over and over again and not just in yourself but in everyone on earth.

'That is why Beings like myself step forward to help shine a torch here and there in the darkness, to attract you to one branch in favour of another, or to turn upward away from the soft, deep earth.

'So, how am I doing? Is my torch flickering well enough to attract your attention?'

Dorothy: *Laughs.* 'I think we both know the answer to that one. Thank you, until tomorrow. Shalom.'

Fear

Dorothy: 'Shalom. I know you will be aware of our earlier conversation about clearing up my office and throwing out past projects, hopes and dreams. A conversation that has left me drained and sad and, perhaps surprisingly, fearful about the space I am creating, not just physically, but psychically as well.'

Librarian: 'Shalom to you and was it not fear that you had to overcome at the start of your spiritual journey? So, surely, it stands to reason that as the spiral turns once more fear will approach again, more familiar this time, but always bearing its challenges.

'There is an irony here and that is that fear evokes many admirable qualities, not least tenacity. Now tenacity can be blind stubbornness, but it can also be aligned to Love. Tenacity and Love together make admirable companions for they are loyal to that which they give their heart to, and you gave your heart to this work a long time ago, indeed before you were born.

'So fear is multi faceted. Each time the spiral turns and requires something different from you then the different levels of fear reassert themselves. Partly to insist that you engage your discrimination before making any rash moves, and partly to ensure that you do not sleepwalk into something that is not heartfelt and soul nourishing.

'I accept that this may sound strange to you, but the greater the fear the deeper the final commitment will be for, as with everything else, you will have worked to make that commitment meaningful. During your conversation this morning you talked about the swathes of work you have collated, filed, lovingly recorded and now are archiving or destroying as if that was a failure.

'Does that not prove my point though? From fear, through reluctance, self-examination, judgement, criticism, and indifference you have both continued and built up an impressive body of work by any standard. I do not know but you are possibly unique amongst the membership, in the care you have taken of the Source material, your understanding of it, your painstaking collations and attention to detail over its presentation. Not to mention your joint creativity and the development of your own aligned materials. All of which you have sought, and sought again, to spread and share exactly as asked.

'I know because I was with you, that as you stored away the material you felt the Light within it, you respected it and you hope it will be useful in times to come, times you may never see. You know yourself that what is important has been retained. Now, there is a clearing of space around you ready for a new chapter, a new turn of the spiral, one which has a foundation as deep as the first crystal of your planet.

'If you feel the fear beloved one trust that it is pointing to the depth of your next step and trust in your heart, your strong hearts, that have taken you both forward and forward together. They are a credit to you and have a Light which shines brightly and fills those that watch over you with pride and gratitude.

'Shalom beloved one, we too have overcome obstacles this morning have we not? Strong hearts and soul connections are wonderful things.'

Dorothy: 'Indeed, thank you and shalom.'

Staying with difficulty

Librarian: 'An imperative to write sometimes makes the words fly up into the heavens and scramble themselves into a myriad of thoughts which could cohere a million ways, does it not? You stop, you pause, you delete your words again asking yourself, where are you in that, where am I? You wonder if your computer failing is a message not to continue? If there is too much disruption to continue? All of this seems to be pulling you away from that centre of Light that was flickering and shining at first. That centre of Light that seeks an audience and the attention of your mind and heart. You write with both, you know, your mind and your heart and it is the Light that coheres the two and calls me forth.

'That beautiful Light you know as the Christos and I do too, for it bathes the Spirit world just as it bathes your world. It holds all within its silent, patient, eternal flow and moves like quicksilver over your world and mine. It is quite simply Love incarnate, an eternal miracle that exceeds my knowledge and my imagination for it is as intimate as it is universal and it is inexhaustible.

'We have spoken of the gift of freewill and yet, the Christos is perhaps the greatest gift of all. At one level you could say it is quite simply the gift of life, and that is true for life on Earth, so why you might ask was it necessary to enhance its flow at the Millennium? Well, the short answer is that mankind has been through more than one evolution and there has been an increasing move away from the true meaning of life and the need of the Soul to experience Love.

'So many people who speak to a spiritual Teacher, or reach out in meditation or prayer, ask whether the purpose of life on earth is to suffer? Whether their own purpose is to endure, or to spend their remaining life in sackcloth and ashes for some misdemeanour they regret? You could say that as mankind approached the Millennium their future was receding, for the planet was suffering and mankind were engaging in collective self neglect and destruction too.

'Mankind really have no true idea of the depth of Love God has for Its children. How the fulfilment of their collective purpose is important to the Spirit world and beyond. How painful their collective denial of their fundamental need to know that they belong to something greater and are loved holds them back from fulfilling their potential and the potential of their individual and collective Soul ...'

Dorothy: 'I'm unable to continue, I'm sorry I am struggling with this.'

Librarian: 'What are you struggling with?'

Dorothy: 'We had a shaky start and I am not certain if this is a true reflection of your words.'

Librarian: 'Do you not think perhaps you are finding the subject challenging? That perhaps your difficulty is in confronting your own need to know that you are loved and that that Love is stronger than any external factor and needs your attention as much as you crave It?

'If we were truly sitting across from one another I would ask that you be seated again and take a sip of your tea. I do not mean to be harsh or unkind, but to point out that being Loved can be a challenge. It is not always roses and chocolates, sometimes it is just reminding you that Love is the foundation of Being and in particular, in this setting, the foundation of learning.

'I imagine it is hard as someone in life to hear how far away from Love they, and all mankind, have travelled. How close they are to the precipice, and I know that feeling powerless is quite a common reaction. Having so many of your personal needs entwined with the very systems that are denuding your planet must be hard to accept, for it is heartbreaking, is it not? Better to leave the conversation before those harsh reminders fill that page.'

Dorothy: 'I'm sorry … '

Librarian: 'Can you see beloved one how your reaction, your fear, and confusion mirrors the very issue I am speaking of. How your fear of getting it wrong cuts you off from the very Love and Light that was embracing you all the while. Your computer failing did not interrupt the flow of Light, nor the intervention of the noise, it continued, but you, with the best of intentions, started to turn away back into your world.

'Mankind collectively started running many, many generations ago and in the wrong direction. They seem deaf to the voices that whisper, "stop, wait, open your hearts and your minds to the Love that surrounds you and listen to Its wisdom, for it is greater than yours and knows your soul's purpose.

'So how are you feeling now?'

Dorothy: 'I have a dual experience of the Light within which is steady at the core but stuttering slightly at the edges. I am grateful I stayed with it as I know I would have felt disappointed with myself if I had not continued, but I also feel a little churned up.'

Librarian: 'What you are describing to me is a candle flame which is steady at its core with more colours flickering at its edges, and that is good. I have to know you can accommodate difficulty as well as praise, for the purpose of these conversations is to share the Truth, and the Truth of existence at this time is complicated and messy and painful to hear. But if you, and others like you, censor the words of one like myself then where do we turn?

'Love is not just acceptance, peace and gentleness, true Love is bold and fearless and unstinting in Its presence. It stands beside you as you face the realities of life. It has your back, but it also stands a little way ahead and holds out Its hand to show you what must be faced if your purpose is to be fulfilled. Your purpose is no different from the collective purpose of humanity and this time together across the Realms is too precious to waste.'

Dorothy: 'I want to demur, but I am going to have to find a place where I can hear and record as accurately as possible what passes between us. A place where I can suspend, judgement, censorship, or expectations now that might be a struggle, but I am willing to try.'

Librarian: 'That is all I can ask, and I thank you.'

Dorothy: 'What on earth for?'

Librarian: 'For summarising Love in one sentence, "allowing someone to be exactly what they are without judgement, censorship, or expectation." Now perhaps you see how freeing spiritual Love can be? If someone aligns their purpose to their soul then their freedom is assured and the Love of the Christos is their faithful companion, friend, and guide.

'My Love surrounds you now and forever. I will leave you to your kettle. Shalom.'

Dorothy: *Smiles.* 'Shalom.'

The past is a portal

The past is just a portal
to pastures broad and new,
how far you then travel
is entirely up to you.

The restrictions that you pass through
may well have held you fast,
but the potential when you clear them,
is unimaginable and vast.

If you take your past fears with you,
like a rucksack on your back,
they will weigh you down, remind you,
of all the things you lack.

So place your rucksack at the pillar,
see a lighted path instead,
your soul is walking with you,
both behind you and ahead.

For your soul extracts the learning
that brings value to the world,
and as you travel onward
that learning will unfurl.

Personality and need

Librarian: 'I see it you know, I see it.'

Dorothy: 'What do you see?'

Librarian: 'The courage it takes to open to me, to clear the space and to trust that your call will be answered. For it is a call beloved one, it is a call, and one that I cherish but which you make instinctively and silently. The best analogy I can think of is that each morning you walk along a passageway, with each footstep being a word of your prayer. As you advance the soft Light becomes steadier and then, usually after a sip of your tea, you pause for a moment before turning a door handle and allowing the Light to flow out and greet you before walking forward.

'You have come to trust that behind that doorway is Light. You do not doubt it, or try the handle on other doorways, you walk steadily forward and open the door to what you describe as the Library of Lives, assured now in your own mind of a welcome. That is the call, for as the Light floods out to great you it also merges with the light of the world that you bring with you, and within that light is your need and the collective need of mankind.

'It is in that pause that your courage steadies your hand, and it is in the pauses between the words of your prayer that you feel the Light accompany your passage past the other doorways. Doorways you have opened before and have closed one by one as they served their purpose.

'But I see the courage, beloved one, I sense the deep breath and the steady heart and that enables me to flood your consciousness and speak my Truth to you. A Truth that is applicable to all, without exception, for when we speak of Love and there is no one on this planet that does not need Love and yet so few with the courage to seek it out.'

Dorothy: 'I would never have used the term "courage" I always believed that any spiritual journey was about surrender, acceptance and belief, courage sounds so much more proactive.'

Librarian: *Laughs.* 'Well I guess your journeys here would soon cease if I did not surprise you from time to time. Surrender, acceptance and belief are important, yes and I could probably add a longer list, but so often people confuse surrender with the abdication of the self. Putting aside their personality and personal need in order to be ready to receive the gift of Love. It is an error of thinking that has been replicated in many religions and organised forms of worship because it gives power to those who proclaim themselves as leaders.

'Do people really believe that having a personality and individual needs was a mistake made by the Creator? That every soul who comes to earth should be a clone of each other and acquiesce to the same paths of learning? How would the Collective Soul ever learn if that were the case, how would it explore Light and dark to its furthest reaches and back again? How would it understand cruelty and kindness? Love and hate? It is not possible.

'Your personality is the chosen vehicle for your soul and for the application of freewill. It is if you like, God given, but that does not mean it is immutable, for it is as influenced by the world as it is cognisant of your soul's purpose. Here I am speaking generally, for the calibration between worldly pleasures and soulful learning, for want of a better phrase, is always individual and a work in progress from the moment of birth to the moment of passing.

'As I recall two months ago you confidently said to a dear friend of yours that you could see no more writing on the horizon, and yet here you are and it is bringing you joy is it not?'

Dorothy: 'Yes and many other things beside.'

Librarian: 'Then it is a good example of your personality accommodating your soul's desire to pursue your spiritual work in a more inspired way than previously, where you have compiled the words of others instead of your own. There is no error in that, every page written, read and complied is archived by your soul and available when there is need for this Light.

'That brings me neatly, and elegantly, even though I say so myself, back to the point about personality being an important vehicle in life. For Spirit responds to need and it is the personality that expresses, or suppresses, those needs in life. Need is like the hand on the handle of the archive of Light which waits to flood out and help all mankind to fulfil their purpose and the purpose of Creation. I pray that more find the courage to open those doorways of Light.'

'Shalom to you this day. I know you are seeing your family and walking not just with your adult family but alongside your developing granddaughter, such joy, such a precious time. Our Love and joy surrounds you all.'

'Thank you, the pandemic certainly makes these visits even more precious. Shalom.'

Tapestry of Light

Dorothy: 'I cannot feel your presence are you there?'

Librarian: 'Where else would I be?'

Dorothy: 'I don't know but I don't suppose I am alone in making this journey.'

Librarian: 'Ah, but you are alone and your pathway here bears the hallmarks of your life, and your life alone. In years to come it may help others, but no one walks the same path. Think of Yeshua, the guiding Light of humanity, the symbol of eternal life, the Lord of Love, it is not sensible at all to consider that the only pathway to eternity is by following His example.'

'So many do though, they cling to one pattern of behaviour without ever questioning if it is right for them. Afraid to ask themselves if their soul is rejoicing in their choice of lifestyle and is learning what it came to learn? But what they are truly clinging to is safety and routine, and they sleepwalk into abdicating their self responsibility to make choices that reflect their individuality, without doing harm to others.'

'Yeshua was always obedient to His purpose, but He was also wilful and willing to challenge the norms of the society He was born into when they contradicted His own innate understanding of the Will of God. He knew, He just knew, from a very young age that He would have to walk His own path and stand for the Light that was growing inside Him.'

'Now, you could say that Yeshua was unique and I would agree with you, but the Light that He bore is universal. Once you have discovered that thread within yourself, then it leads you exactly where you need to go and invites you to be all of what you have the potential to be.'

'It will not, I am sure, have escaped your notice that there is a correlation between the thread of Light I have just spoken of and the genetic links that bind generations and often cultures together. It is indeed through this link that the Light flows. So, when homecoming souls visit your imagined library that is the Light stream they follow, back through past lives, so they can weave a tapestry of understanding and knowledge strand by strand.'

'If you recall your early imagery of different streams of Light moving between the bookshelves, well, that is what your imagination gave form to. Stream upon stream of DNA collecting and compiling knowledge from experience and then preparing the souls due to incarnate to go and fill in any gaps in the picture, or to correct any mistakes. A task, may I say, that is harder than a room full of scientists sending a machine to Mars, for at least the scientists do not have to calibrate the velocity of freewill.

'So imagine thousands upon thousands of weavers working with the most exquisite colours, each collective busy completing their assigned image, but constantly sharing with others around them. Imagine them pausing to admire a new piece of the picture, hugging each other as they complete one portion, perhaps clapping when someone on earth solves a problem that also sheds Light in Spirit. Imagine other souls from surrounding collectives overhearing the delight and gathering round to see the discovery for themselves and marvel at how an image once dull has just become vibrant and complete.'

'One day, one day, this will not be a library, even in your imagination, but a completed tapestry of Light, stretching into infinity, every thread carefully in its place, every picture defined and clear and contributing to a beautiful pattern. So exquisite it will take your breath away as it merges back into the Light of God, which expands and grows ever brighter.'

Dorothy: 'And none of us will ever see it.'

Librarian: 'I think we will beloved one for in each part is the whole and we are all a part. As it merges into the Light we will both become part of the whole and see it for the first time.'

Dorothy: 'That's a great image, thank you.'

Librarian: 'It's a great image because it is the Truth and the Truth is beautiful. Shalom beloved one, shalom.'

The Equinox

Librarian: 'Shalom to you this day, no doubt about my presence then?'

Dorothy: 'Shalom to you and no, no doubt. Although I am tempted to add that, many people might interpret these tingles as the start of a headache.'

Librarian: *Laughs.* 'You say the nicest things and although I know it was a joke, or at least I hope it was, as always there is a grain of Truth within it that I would like to expand on.'

'Those of us from Spirit who find a voice in life are a headache, are we not? If the ground has not been sufficiently prepared, or someone adds substances like alcohol, or drugs to the mix, then the reaction within the person could be damaging. That is why it is important for all those seeking spiritual inspirations that they understand the need for protection and guidance.'

'At the moment there are significant changes going on within you, within your partner and within the world and these are all very positive. In your case, sadly not the world's, they are the culmination of years of study, dedication, discipline, and belief and even though they are subtle, gentle and individually unremarkable they are effective.'

'Think about the last few weeks and months, we have been speaking for just two of them, and the quality of your partner's channelling has changed over that period too. We are approaching the Equinox, and although in the past it elicited much mirth when your Teachers indicated that things would take a positive turn after the Equinox, nevertheless it is an important milestone.'

'In the past it was your view that the only reason the Teachers promised improvement was because things always got worse just before an Equinox and so were bound to improve at some point after it. There was some Truth in that, there was a condensing of the energies before the Equinox and a releasing afterwards, a releasing driven by a spiritual imperative.'

'So, if you were right then perhaps you are right now? Perhaps these conversations are all part of that condensing along with the changes in the channelling? For if the energies condense around negativity perhaps they also condense around positivity and then the progress, the rewards, arising from your perseverance become obvious. Can you accept that as a premise?'

Dorothy: 'Yes I think I can. It's always been easier for me to prepare for more difficulty than ease, but yes, I understand the logic of what you're saying, even though my feelings might take longer to catch up.'

Librarian: Huh! 'There are times when I think that a plague of locusts would be a handy shortcut for spiritual Guides to have at their disposal. It is so easy for mankind, yourself included, to dismiss or deny, the subtle, positive, gentle shifts that I know bring you joy and contentment every day.

'There are times when we feel frustration too, for we know the rarity of true spiritual progress in life and so want our charges to rejoice in their achievements from time to time. What would it take for you to accept on an emotional level what you can accept intellectually?'

Dorothy: 'Well if it's any comfort, I am not sure a plague of locusts would do the trick? Seriously though, I do take your point, and I guess the straight answer to your question is probably time. I do understand how the need to defend myself against criticism and judgement almost all my life became instinctive and self-destructive, but it's still there for me. There is still an issue of self-worth which dissipates over time, usually most successfully when my attention is elsewhere.

'Coincidentally, or perhaps not, this conversation is almost mirroring the promised changes in the pandemic and the restrictions we have all been living under. I have been trying not to get too excited about those in case another variant plunges us into yet another lockdown. So, I am well versed in managing my expectations.'

Librarian: 'I know you anticipate this, but where is the coincidence? To be fair if you and your partner had not used this period of enforced restriction so well the lifting of restrictions would be less meaningful. But that is my point, you have both used this period well and remained committed to your work and development and as such the timings mirror each other. As the gentle changes embed and you become more confident, it may well coincide with the lifting of restrictions. Perhaps then I won't be the only voice pointing to the impressive shifts you have made. There's another phrase you use I believe about believing pigs can fly, but how your heart only rejoices if you actually see one. I don't think I can think of a better image for us to conclude on, can you?'

Dorothy: 'No I think you've made your point.'

Librarian: 'Then my job here is done. I wish you a peaceful and fruitful day with your tasks, which I know are very taxing, but are not coincidental either. Shalom.'

Turning points

Librarian: 'Shalom to you this day, a day when the past has come visiting once more evoking feelings and memories and casting a shadow over your spirit. But why should they? Have the lessons not been learned, and has not your journey continued onto higher plains and through deeper valleys of understanding?

'I am not merely here to repeat my words of encouragement, I am here to say that memories in life, distort and distort again around feelings. Already this morning you have tried to unhook two emotionally significant events from one another because you found written proof that you had misremembered the dates. But the reason for the confusion was that the two events were of similar weight and indeed similar content. Although they appear superficially different, they were both about your place in the world, your progress through life, and the blueprint you had envisaged for your combined future.

'I believe you described it at the time as "being cut off at the knees". The details are unimportant, as the learning I wish to extract is that people tend to aggregate emotionally charged events together to illustrate their own storyline. A storyline that will be comforting and familiar as it is formed entirely of their own self beliefs, perspective, and history.

'So, how then do you, while in life, separate out the true meaning behind the turning points that occur throughout your life? How do you disentangle your own self belief in failure, success, or mediocrity? How do you disentangle your feelings from the message?

'I wish there was an easy answer, but, in life, there is not one, for this recalibration really takes place after you have passed to Spirit. Then your memories of events are accurate and sparkle with life as they reveal their hidden lessons. But, while in life, there is work you, and here I speak generally, can do to uncover those lessons. It does require emotional honesty about how your personality and soul have had to navigate their path together and how resistant, or acquiescent, your personality has been to outside interference, if we can describe your soul that way.

'So much of the passage through life plays out in the environment. So many people look to change their external environment because frankly it is easier than changing their internal one and they seek out those companions that will reinforce their self identification. Now there is no blame of judgement here, for your soul chose the environment that would present particular lessons, but how many people know that? How many people feel they have been unfairly treated, disadvantaged, or impoverished. How many consider themselves to be failures or rejects? Are children not encouraged from a young age to stick up for themselves, to prove something to the world in order to succeed?

'So is it any wonder that, in life, the emotional self becomes more defined by the personality than by the soul? That it is treated like a mere character in the storyboard created by the self rather than a living field of energy, connected to the soul that has a story and needs of its own? Needs that, if ignored, will burst forth when circumstances allow, or the time is right, and demand attention.

'These are the turning points in life, and it can be useful at these times to see the emotional body as a third point in the triangle. You have the external imperative, perhaps you have lost your job; you have your intellectual and lifestyle choices, how you will pay your bills? But then you have this third component, if you are emotionally astute, which is, what is this challenge demanding from me? How will the choices I make now serve my purpose in life and fulfil my soul? That way your emotional body has a voice that provides a bridge between the immediate and the greater.

'Now I do accept, really I do that in the heat of the moment achieving that kind of clarity can be almost impossible, but it can assist in creating more accurate memories later. For example, in your situation, if you were emotionally honest, would you argue that change was unnecessary? That everything was going as planned and you felt fulfilled? You and I both know the answer to that would be, "no", so would you agree that change was imperative?'

Dorothy: 'I don't think I thought that at the time.'

Librarian: 'Indeed, that is honest, but what of now?'

Dorothy: 'Yes, probably.'

Librarian: 'Why probably?'

Dorothy: 'The way it was done was cruel and unnecessarily harsh.'

Librarian: 'There is some justification in that statement, but the cruelty was at the emotional point of the triangle, from all sides, would you agree?'

Dorothy: 'Again, probably yes.'

Librarian: 'Still probably, hmm. But that is the point is it not, feelings tend to cloud the reality of situations and prevent actions from taking place that are necessary to achieve the greater picture?'

Dorothy: 'In this instance, it would be easier for me to agree if I thought the long-term outcome had been successful. I don't think it has been.'

Librarian: 'Really, then you are not feeling satisfied with your progress at the moment?'

Dorothy: *Laughs.* 'OK, I see where you are going with this. I am happy with my progress at the moment and yes, to anticipate your next question, I feel my soul has a new-found freedom and a voice, which I am really enjoying.'

Librarian: 'Well, if you are correctly following the trajectory of my thoughts, you will know that I think that the removal of your knees has worked out pretty well. Metaphorically speaking, they slowed your earthly progress, made you more inclined to open to Spirit and seeded new, better, legs.' *Laughs.* 'There's a metaphor for you! So do you probably agree or actually agree?'

Dorothy: *Smiles.* 'I agree.'

Librarian: 'Good. If that is an honest response, as I believe it is, then what that agreement does is allow the emotional point of the triangle to appreciate the benefits and disentangle itself from the mechanism of change. That means the Light within the lessons, including any clumsiness during implementation, is released and you can absorb the benefit of the experience.

'I know you would agree that if change is necessary, it must be confronted and not avoided, for even where there are unintended consequences there is learning, but in avoiding change learning becomes static and a dead weight to progress.'

Dorothy: 'I do agree and thank you.'

Librarian: 'I see the Light has brushed away the shadows from earlier, so peace has returned. My love is with you always, shalom.'

Written in the stars above

Come gently to my arms dear friend,
you fear your pain will never end.
But as you rest your hand in mine,
you know you walk with the Divine.

There's no demand of you I make,
I offer Love for you to take,
to spread and share amongst your friends,
the Source of which is without end.

And if my hand you then let go,
I'll never leave, it can't be so.
For once that bond is made in Love,
it's written in the stars above.

It sheds its soft unbending Light,
to guide your steps towards what's right.
It eases pain and opens doors,
that show you what your life is for.

This gentle Christos strong and true,
exists in me, exists in you.
No distinction does it make.
No single man will it forsake.

First responders

Librarian: 'Shalom to you this day, a tricky night by all accounts.'

Dorothy: 'Shalom and yes, I am tired from being awake, but I am not sure why I was awake, there was nothing worrying me.'

Librarian: 'It does not always have to be your personal worries or anxieties that cause this effect, it can be a side effect of opening to Spirit, of expanding your consciousness each morning and of that connection remaining with you. I am not hidden behind a one-way door that you open and close I, and your other inspirers, walk alongside you every moment of the day.

'But, just as I am not a temporary aberration your connection is not temporary either, although always subject to your permission and mediation. However, this expansion into the Spirit realm means that you are sensitive to the movements within those Realms, although ignorant of their causes, and sometimes participate in your dream state.

'I know you do not expect me to await your arrival each morning with bated breath, but know that I have other charges and other duties which I perform. I am constantly involved in the movements of the planets and in the healing of your world. You would be surprised really at how dedicated we in Spirit are to the well being of mankind and the future of the Earth. We see what you do not and our horizons are greater than yours. We see and interpret the patterns of cause and effect long before it is obvious on the earth.

'I have a very privileged position of learning a great deal from the homecoming souls. Although their information is shared primarily with their Higher Self, I am privileged to have an overview of all of this sharing. At times that can be overwhelming, for the rate of increase in some areas can cause concern and require spiritual attention to try to divert an immediate disaster.

'Although freewill is sacrosanct amongst mankind there are times when Spirit need to take the action they can to ... how can I put this ... give man time to wake up to the disaster on his doorstep. When this is needed a great deal of communication takes place between those charged with ... I think you have a phrase "first responders" ... so the communication takes place between those in Spirit who are the first responders. Within that communication is quite a lot of debate, even the ethics of how to mitigate any impact on earth without overriding freewill. For although mankind has freewill that cannot be allowed to extend to irreparable damage to the whole of the Earth.

'These communications, mind to mind debates, can be really consuming and there can be expressions of anxiety from those of us involved. We have emotions too, just as we discussed yesterday, and these emotions have to be worked through in the same way as you need to do in life. So many of our first responders lived on the earth and have returned with a love and a wonder of the natural world that never dims. If they had mouths, they would be wide open at the ignorance mankind displays towards their world and the perceived cruelty through sheer neglect.

'When we spoke yesterday we spoke of how emotions distort memories of the past. So, imagine now the depth of the emotions felt in Spirit as we debate making an intervention knowing we are powerless to circumvent freewill, and possessing the long range vision and advance knowledge of all the potential outcomes. If that was not complicated, enough add into the equation the fact that Spirit are Love and Love is the Law. So, it is no surprise that our feelings are intense, but also crucial, for Love is the healing force that will be applied to the situation. Our debates are about how best to apply that Love.

'I am struggling to think of an analogy ... I suppose the best description is of being a grandparent and watching your children, or grandchildren, prepare to make a mistake. You know the outcome, you have walked that path before, but do you intervene because you love them and wish them to come to no harm? If you do you stop them learning from experience and anyway there is always the possibility that things will turn out better than you predicted, so you might end up being the one doing the learning.

'For example, when we discuss emotions you absorb my perspective so it is no surprise that your consciousness will then be ultra-sensitive to any movement within the emotional field of Spirit. I make no apology for this because if all of humanity had that depth of connection then Love would be the Law and together, Spirit and mankind, would heal each other and the planet.'

Dorothy: 'Thank you, you never cease to amaze me in your responses, often to mere asides or what I would consider inconsequential musings.'

Librarian: 'You would be surprised how it is the small things that trap mankind, how slights, hurts and misunderstandings pervade history, undermine progress and foster division generation after generation. If I had a droplet of Light for every time an incoming soul has reviewed their life and felt regret for the small things, I would have more Light to share than your sun emits. Beware regret, beloved one, beware regret. Shalom to you this day, shalom.'

Stepping stones

Librarian: 'Shalom to you beloved one, shalom. I see your struggles and I feel your pain, but encouragement alone is not enough. You keep walking, yes, but even as you walk you falter, not in your heart but in your mind, and you feel that this is a failure. My beloved one it is not a failure it is a consequence of living in the world and being subjected to the beliefs of others and the changing mores of your society. Your feelings are affected by the feelings of others all the time. Pulled and pushed and pulled again.

'How can this be failure? It is anything but, you are here to live in this world, to understand and experience its effect on you and others and to grow wise and compassionate in so doing. To grow to accept and share Love even when it has been denied you, or is mocked as a foundation of life. To find out for yourself what truly matters and to be true to that.

'In my view, failure is an unexamined life, and by life I include the Realms of Spirit. I do not expect everyone to be a medium or to go around in a semi-trance reciting Teachings or poetry, but just a glimpse of an awakening to something more, something greater, something that silently unifies and brings hope.

'You live this life, you both live this life, without a second thought and yet, you also feel the pain of failure, of being out of place from time to time. You know that what is important to you is not so to others, even close friends, and so you stay silent, offering a morsel from time to time to see if they want more. But they are busy, their eyes and hearts are facing elsewhere, as yours once were, so you move on and you carry on.

I know, I know, beloved one, that as much as you seek recognition you fear it. As much as you want to share what is precious to you, you fear the reactions, the criticism, the mockery, so your mind pulls you this way and that before you have even left your front door. This is the mind trap is it not and it assails so many people and leads to the regret I spoke of yesterday.

'These are the experiences of life you have come to learn from. You may be surprised when you look back in past lives to find these mind traps are a common thread and one, perhaps, you are here to overcome this time. To find your portion of the Light and to trust it and the Source from which it flows. In your case, in this life, it is not mediated through religion, or a strict education, although it has been mediated through your involvement in a spiritual Group, but take all that away and what are you left with? Yes, you have your family history which still nibbles at your expectations but has largely been overcome, primarily by honest self-examination. And, may I say, the firm intervention of your Teachers who have led you away from the very limited spiritual perspective which you grew up with, a perspective concocted as a defence against a painful world.

'How am I doing so far?'

Dorothy: 'Good morning and well, I think. You are right about the constant inner debates I have, partly to do with my family background, but also more recent events that have had a dual impact of opening and closing doors at the same time. I had a strong image many years ago as an inspirer of my partner spoke to me a series of doors slammed shut. Her words were, "be the beautiful soul you are," or something along those lines. Yet at that moment doors were slamming shut along a long corridor, it was shocking.'

Librarian: 'Of course it was, it was the straightener you needed at that time and what did you imagine being behind the doors?'

Dorothy: 'At the time I would have said my future, my dreams, but now … '

Librarian: 'Now how would you answer?'

Dorothy: 'I would be more generous and assume that the doors I imagined were more likely to be delusion, ambition, misunderstandings, leaving just the narrow path I needed to take and no other.'

Librarian: 'Now what do you imagine was at the end?'

Dorothy: 'Light.'

Librarian: 'What would you have imagined at the time?'

Dorothy: 'There was nothing there, not darkness exactly. I seem to recall now a feeling of being turned round ninety degrees too, but I might be making that up.'

Librarian: 'You might be but that does not matter for the message is clear is it not? It could have led to you giving up. I do know what a shock it was as I can feel it in you now, but I also know that as you followed the recollection you felt gentle hands on your shoulder pointing you in the right direction? Am I right?'

Dorothy: 'Yes, it's that feeling that evoked an image of being turned around, and I have it now.'

Librarian: 'Do you feel you are being turned away or towards now?'

Dorothy: 'Towards.'

Librarian: 'That is good, for indeed doors slammed shut because they needed to, and it may surprise you to learn that behind those doors were all the things that would have affected your recovery from the shock. For example, a descent into alcohol, or drugs, something you have never considered for that very reason.

'You, and most people in a spiritual path, hope for a single moment of Truth, of awakening, of enlightenment, but, and here I am sorry to disappoint, that single moment called bodhi, in Sanskrit, never occurs. For when it does, it will be collective, not individual. Instead, it happens in small ways, momentary images that are recalled years later that, like a laser, pointing the right way forward. It was then up to your freewill to follow it or not.

'You have a great deal to thank that beautiful soul for, but equally it knew that limping, sprinting, or dawdling you would follow it above all else.'

Dorothy: 'That's lovely to hear and yes, I see now how those momentary images have been like stepping stones on the path and I feel fortunate to have had them. Thank you.'

Librarian: 'You are not alone in having stepping stones, all have access to them, but so few make use of them or even consider they need to.

'My Love is with you. Shalom.'

Embrace the Light within

Although you sense the Light around you,
do you embrace the Light within?
Do you trust its subtle guidance
on where you're going, where you've been?

Do you feel its hand reach down to you
when darkness does abound?
Do you hear the Aum of solace,
that eternal, healing sound?

Always there beyond your senses,
part of every cell that's you.
Supremely loyal through every life,
whatever you may do.

Sparks of Creation

Librarian: 'Shalom to you this spring day, where shall we walk together? Shall we circuit a forest of trees and brambles, considering the passages through life and their consequences? Or walk on a beach and look out over open vistas with just the horizon in sight, the sky changing colour as the sun rises on your day, the waves lapping gently and placing their treasure at our feet? Or perhaps a desert where the heat of the day is unbearable, but the cool of the night is such a relief. The sky above us sparkling with diamonds, flashes, and colour, as deep as the universe lifting our spirits with it?

'Life is a marvel, is it not? And yet most people seem to walk along the same tracks every day, repeating the same actions with the same people over and over again, neither feeling a lack of meaning, nor any wonder for the earth that gave them life.

'Now, do not misunderstand me. I have not suddenly been recruited by your airline industry to sell you a package tour where I carefully pick up your current habits and place them in another environment with a different climate and strange costumes. Not at all, I am talking about the ability of the mind to travel and empathise, create wonder and new experiences all from the comfort of an armchair.

'I hear your thoughts when you wonder how someone who has never walked in a forest could imagine being there. Or never having got their feet wet could transport themselves to a seashore where sharp shells cut the skin and water cools the ankles. Well, that is my point in a way, I can because I can travel within the universal mind, as can you and everyone else. I can follow the tracks of my charges and experience the salt air on their breath, by watching the shimmer of their aura as they wander along those routes in their minds eye. I can see the shadow of pollution as they explore their city streets, and I can wonder at how people choose to live lives that are so hard and repetitive and seemingly pointless.

'But, and there is always a but with me is there not regardless of your correct forms of grammar? But, I also understand the importance of love in these situations. I see how caring for a sick relative, or loving someone who is acting foolishly, tugs at the heart strings and means people do incredible things in service of love. You watched a documentary yesterday about a mother living in absolute poverty and isolation fighting for her imprisoned son, who she believes to be innocent. Her community turned against her and yet, she displayed no bitterness towards them and their belief in his guilt did not prevent her belief in his innocence. I do not need to live her life, and neither do you, to appreciate the learning that that woman is extracting from her time on earth. The depths of despair she has endured and the depth of her belief and faith in the truth finding its way into the public domain.

'What do you think the conversations were with her soul before incarnation? Do you think it described her current life and then sought her agreement to be born into that life? What karma is playing out for her and her son and indeed the victim of the murder that took place? As you watched you wondered about the other suspects, those not identified all those years ago but identified now, all of whom have stories to tell that have been hidden to society, but not to Spirit. Normal lives on the surface that walk on hidden tracks of fear, secrets, and regret which will provide such deep learning on their return home, if not before.

'Such richness, such depth of learning being repeated over and over again in so many dark corners of your world. All of which, all of which, have the potential to bring Light to the soul for they are all paths of learning and nothing is wasted, not one step.

'You cannot live your life through the stories of other people, of course not, but you can access the tapestry of learning that is being woven every day upon your world and indeed throughout the universe. Sparks of Creation like the diamonds in the desert sky that flare for a moment and then fall to earth, picked up by the Soul and added to Its wealth of understanding. What a marvel life is.'

Dorothy: 'Well you have left me speechless, there's nothing to add really except my thanks.'

Librarian: 'The thanks are all mine beloved one, I may think these things, I may feel these things but without your attention and your commitment they would also flare and fall, but not to earth. I thank you from the bottom of my heart. Shalom.'

Why these conversations?

Librarian: 'Shalom to you this day, I missed you yesterday and I know you missed me too, how lovely, such depth after what would seem like such a brief encounter in earthly terms, but not in spiritual ones. It is like a mini homecoming, is it not? There is so much you recognise, so much familiarity even though descriptions might fail you, there is a sense of peace and belonging and even excitement is there not?'

Dorothy: 'Yes, although it was the right decision yesterday not to visit, later in the day I had regrets. I do know that the concept of visiting is not accurate, but it helps me to delineate my time of meditation from everything else and encourages me to persevere. When I feel your signal, I often see the most gentle green, like chrysoprase, with a gentle golden hue, is that your colour?'

Librarian: 'There is a great deal of green in my aura. My role is to soothe and settle and green is comforting to most homecoming souls. As you can imagine many who have been raised with strict religious beliefs arrive expecting judgement and a wise old man waiting at the gate to agree, or refuse, their entry. So, there can be a long period of readjustment as they begin to allow the gold, which you know as the Christos, to bathe them in the Love that they so need, but many fear. My Light has to be gentle, as any Light can feel harsh if you have lived a life in the darkness, or are fearful of being judged and stripped naked of all the accoutrements of life and asked to account for your actions and inactions. The shock can be the greatest for those expecting nothingness.'

Dorothy: 'As you were speaking, I began to ask myself the purpose of my visits. Is their value only in making me feel good at the start of my day? I am not at this time working with anyone, or sharing these words with anyone except my partner and, as you know, he is already an accomplished channel and so nothing is really new to him.'

Librarian: 'If these words and this transmission of energy does nothing but flow into your world until you pass, then it will have had a value to the whole world. It matters not how accurately you capture the Light in sentences, although I know it does to you, or how representative your images are of life in Spirit. What is important for you is that, before your own homecoming, you have a vibrant spiritual life which you depend on and which can depend on you.

'For we do rely on you you know? The relationship is mutual, not one way, you do not, for example, row across the Styx without us providing the boat, the harbour, the guiding Light and the welcome. But should you follow through with your thoughts about publishing and distribution I would be delighted for then our joint journey may find its way into the hearts and minds of others and bring peace and comfort. You could, or course, accuse me of selfishness here because were all my homecoming souls to start arriving filled with peace and eagerly anticipating their next step I would be, in earthly parlance, redundant and then what would I do? I, like you, would have to look for another purpose to my existence ... hmm ... maybe I could take a well-earned holiday on the earth and bathe in the sea, and walk in the forests and climb all the mountains that I hear so much about.'

Dorothy: 'Do you think that it would ever be possible that you would visit the earth either as a soul incarnate or as a Being of Light?'

Librarian: 'Well, nothing is impossible, whether that would be part of my journey I cannot say, but Masters and Teachers have certainly visited your world before, as have angelic Beings. We never stop trying to bring our influence to bear for the good of mankind and our methods are creative, responsive, and flexible. Not every Master and Teacher came in the flesh as Yeshua did. Everything, and I use this word advisedly, depends not on the willingness of Spirit to assist mankind to turn away from disaster, but on the freewill of mankind and their ability to seek beyond themselves for guidance and meaning.

'You wondered about the purpose of these visits, well, this is the answer to your question, the change within mankind has to come from mankind, it cannot come entirely from Spirit. Every person who seeks beyond themselves and trusts the Light that fills them, who allows that Light to shape their thoughts and actions and seeks to share that with mankind, in whichever way suits their talents, is quite literally a gift from God. And I pray, and those who work with me pray, that mankind receives these gifts with an open heart and an open mind and allows the Light that is their birthright to flow into the world and bring the peace they all desire.'

Dorothy: 'Beautiful, thank you. However, I don't think I will be reserving you a towel by a swimming pool anytime soon.'

Librarian: *Laughs.* 'Indeed not beloved one, indeed not, by that time, should it ever come, neither of us will have hands, or arms or legs of our own. We will have to rely on the reception of Light within the hearts and minds of others and perhaps then you will appreciate what a delight your visits here are to such an ancient soul. Shalom to you this day, until tomorrow, I hope.'

Feeling heard

Dorothy: 'I have to prepare myself for my first online counselling appointment and I am nervous and worried about doing a good job.'

Librarian: 'Then it is good we have time to commune together first because, this I can assure you of, a person seeking help with grief and loss is not seeking advice, techniques or exercises, but to be seen and heard. To be allowed to speak to someone, not directly affected, about how they feel and what their fears are for the future.

'My recollection when you taught mediators was that you would talk to them about people needing reassurance that they were not "mad or bad". Now grief is different from conflict in some ways but not in every way, when anyone feels out of control of their feelings how that is received within their society becomes critical.

'This happened earlier today in your conversation where your vulnerabilities about this work evoked fragile feelings about other aspects of your life. Where you would normally forebear those feelings today you shared them when you were, in truth, too sensitive to bear any reaction. You just wanted to be heard, and my guess is that this is all this person will want from you later this morning.

'Loss and grief have a way of undercutting confidence in all aspects of life, even the continuation of life itself, for your own mortality takes on a new prominence does it not? So, what qualities do you feel are important to enable someone to feel heard?'

Dorothy: 'I know the technical answers about maintaining eye contact and asking open and exploratory questions and reflecting back, but I guess that that is not what you're asking.'

Librarian: 'Really, why would you say that?'

Dorothy: 'Because I suspect that you are pointing to the foundation, not the techniques themselves.'

Librarian: *Laughs.* 'There's no getting past you is there? So, what is the foundation then?'

Dorothy: 'Well, pretty much the same as my conversations with you, a sense of inner peace and an open heart and mind. The content itself is pretty immaterial, as I think our conversations prove, the subject area does not matter, what matters is the sense of Light that is generated by the conversation.'

Librarian: *Laughs* 'There are times beloved one when I wonder what words of wisdom I can offer that you would not have been able to produce yourself. You've said it all, so why the anxiety earlier then? I am now wondering what should happen in our interactions that can complement your already copious awareness.'

Dorothy: 'I feel a settling in my heart when I have shared my anxieties and deepest thoughts with you. A releasing of my own self-criticism because you always respond positively and draw meaning from it, without judging me for feeling fragile in the first place.'

Librarian: 'You feel heard?'

Dorothy: 'And accepted, and that it turn makes me feel acceptable to myself.'

Librarian: 'Another way of saying this is that your emotional body and your mind reharmonises, not only with yourself but with your soul. You are no longer trying to separate off your difficult feelings for fear of interrupting the flow of Light that you seek, but allowing the Light to penetrate those feelings and bring peace. We are discussing this, for the benefit of this conversation, as being between two souls, mine and yours, but in fact it is all internal. The alignment of the subtle health, emotional and mental bodies is entirely within the grasp of every person. As that alignment takes place so the channel to the Spirit realms and the soul clears, as it does when we speak, and the Light flows bringing a sense of peace and Love.

'Mmm, I quite fancy myself with a flip chart and a circle of eager students around me hanging on every word. How did I do at settling your heart beloved one and refocussing your attention on the important elements and away from the peripherals?'

Dorothy: *Laughs.* 'Brilliantly of course. Thank you.'

Librarian: 'Then I look forward to our joint session later this morning for I would not miss this for the world. But before I step back there is one reminder I would like to offer, although I know you know this, and that is that timing is crucial. People may reach out before they're ready to make that internal shift, but if they see the peace in you it will shine as a beacon of hope in the days to come. Shalom beloved one.'

A friend in need

Dorothy: 'Shalom and apologies, I am finding it hard to settle, but I feel your presence.'

Librarian: 'Then let me do the work. Close your eyes, breathe and say your prayer ...

'What did you see?'

Dorothy: 'Velvety cloth in a deep red.'

Librarian: 'Stop resisting, are you afraid of walking with someone coming close to the end of their life in this earth, of letting them know they are in your thoughts?'

Dorothy: 'In a way, but not because I am afraid of that task, but because I don't want to make assumptions as we weren't friends as such.'

Librarian: 'So all your dedicated learning about the interconnectedness of all things, of the Soul Group that exists around your spiritual work, all of this is still open to question after all these years?'

Dorothy: 'No. I believe all that.'

Librarian: 'Then what is stopping you exploring that connection now at a time when the person in question needs comfort and company? Given your acceptance of my ability to "be" in many places at once, do you not think that people who are very ill travel in their minds to many locations and visit many people for succour?'

Dorothy: 'Yes I do and I can relax now and allow that colour to flow and send my love.'

Librarian: 'You were conscious of doing this during the night were you not?'

Dorothy: 'Yes.'

Librarian: 'And were not uncomfortable then?'

Dorothy: 'No, but it was more dreamlike and so involuntary, if you will.'

Librarian: 'I know that to others I might sound harsh but I do not mean to be for your heart is open and your freewill is focussed on giving whatever support you can to a friend in need. It is the mind that cuts and separates in the cold light of day, when it is nighttime and you move between dreaming and waking the mind is more malleable, both to fear, but also to possibility. If it feels that it can reach someone lying in a hospital bed and bring comfort it does not hesitate, but in the daytime it is almost as if the personality needs a written permission slip.

'Love needs no permission, it just is and whether it is accepted, or rejected, by the recipient it makes no difference to its existence. So allow your love to flow and remember that your colour is a vibrant blue, when that combines with ruby red it creates amethyst, and amethyst represents so much at this time and will bring much comfort.

'I know why you hesitate, but you can only bring what you can and as those who love her bring their individual colours also, they increase her vibrancy and inner peace. What better healing can there be?'

Dorothy: 'I know, thank you. I am endlessly hesitant, even I get fed up with that at times.'

Librarian: 'Your healing energy is not hesitant, it is gentle, strong, and persistent. It is no surprise to me that in the world you live in today it has made you feel vulnerable at times, fragile even. You have been subject to many claiming prior ownership and superior knowledge of a universal field of energy that is freely available to all. The problem, if that's what it is, are not the claims themselves, but your tendency to believe them. To make yourself lesser, and that is an act of pride, for it places you above God and in the driving seat.

'Be the beautiful soul you are and that will be more than enough for you and for those who reach out when in need. Shalom to you beloved one, you can rest assured I will be walking beside you wherever life takes you and your loved ones.'

Life in Spirit

Librarian: 'Beloved one, greetings, come sit awhile and drink your tea. Listen to the sounds of the birds, the sounds of the night and to the silence that surrounds your part of the world at this time. Strange is not to think of other cultures awake, bustling in the heat, while London sleeps in the rain. But everywhere, everywhere, there has been a new threat in the streets and stalking the homes of those who are loved and those who live alone. A silent virus that awoke so much in people, not just fear, but the importance of love too. People have been forced to find other ways to communicate when they were separated and suddenly more isolated. Perhaps, just perhaps, gentleness will be this virus' legacy and its crown, as people have experienced for themselves how precious love, care and human contact really is.

'So where shall we travel this morning, is it enough to come and sit, to feel the movement of the planets and the song of homecoming souls? For there is a song you know, a note that echos in the corridors of this place like the sounds of the whales in the ocean. The Aum, always present, joined by the notes and the harmony of souls as they reunite with friends and families from perhaps centuries ago. Old friends and companions, a mother here, a son or daughter there, a servant or nursemaid, all weaving their mind songs that fill this silent Realm. Strange it is not that sound can be silent, profound communication can be felt, not heard and that hearts that no longer beat can open and fill with love?

'All of this known to every person on your earth, but forgotten at birth, creating in some a sense of loss that they can never really place, or resolve. That leaves them feeling untethered to the world and to its people, unable to accept temporal love for they remember spiritual Love and ache for that. A terrible loneliness for those that cannot look within for fear of what they might see, fearful that their unworthiness will prevent their return to the life of Love that exists beyond their grasp. They can live in a kind of stasis, an avoidance of life, a misunderstanding that the spiritual gifts and memories are there for them to explore in life. To help them and guide them to ground their Light in life and bring that Light to others, so much to offer, so much refused and often so many regrets when they come here.'

Dorothy: 'What can you do to help them, what happens when they return?'

Librarian: 'Souls return to their Higher Self which nurtured them before incarnation and waits patiently for their return. The Higher Self knows intimately the progress of the soul on earth, but does not intervene consciously without the permission of the soul, and the personality, to do so. So, some Higher Selves will be preparing for a soul's return before that soul itself knows it is returning. Some Higher Selves will be in dialogue with a soul that is ill, perhaps in a coma, and so the transition is expected when it comes.

'As you know the soul itself creates the environment which it returns to and there is always a period of adjustment where their "new" home mirrors their physical world to some degree. If you look along our corridors you will find souls sleeping there just as on your streets. Or large constructions of Light keeping other souls pinioned behind the imaginary walls they need to manage their transition. Personally, I love the gardens, the courtyards, the woodland, and the natural plants that people imagine there. The water and the seas predominate too, bringing rhythm with them in their minds and comfort to them.

'My role, for that is what you asked, is to wander, to keep a weathered eye on all the Higher Selves, all the homecoming souls, and to soothe those who even here cannot accept the Love that awaits them. Even in a sea of Love there are some souls intent on holding on to a boulder and sinking into despair. I, and other angelic beings, watch, and monitor and hold out our Love waiting for that heart to feel safe enough to open and embrace, and be embraced, by its Higher Self.

Dorothy: 'So are you an angelic Being then?'

Librarian: 'In a way, but not with wings and a trumpet, unless that's your vision today?'

Dorothy: *Laughs.* 'No, I can't say it is, I have stopped imagining how you might look as it happens I am just used to your voice and your presence.'

Librarian: 'Well I am a little relieved, because as Light Beings we could all be described as angelic. But the angelic beings I spoke of are so dedicated to their work of assisting souls to adjust and accept the Light that I don't class myself amongst them. I do work alongside them, as we all work in harmony, fulfilling my role which is to maintain a sea of Love for all homecoming souls while remaining responsive to the needs of the earth. That part is important to me otherwise these precious dialogues would not be possible and that would sadden me.'

Dorothy: 'And me too, such an important part of my life now. I am so grateful to you.'

Librarian: 'May the Light that is captured here flow out into your world and bring peace to all. Until tomorrow beloved one, shalom.'

Surviving not thriving

Librarian: 'Shalom to you this day, I sit beside you as you sit beside me and the Light flows to and fro. I listen with my heart, for I have no ears, to what troubles you, to the peace within you and the need that flickers on the surface. I see your heart and feel it beat in time with mine. Two souls floating in a universe of unimaginable proportions, two souls communicating one with another about everyday things; how I spend my time and you spend yours.

'Time, that currency that exists only in your world, not mine. Time that imperative to change, to grow, to live, to sleep, to leave and to return home. That component within Creation that creates and destroys cultures and civilisations, turn and turn about, like a farmer tilling the soil to plant new crops. Creating new landscapes, new harvests, having learnt what grows and what withers in the heat, the rain, or the drought.

'Time that shows on your face and in your body, but not your eyes, for your eyes carry the Light of eternity, the Light of your soul. They will show weariness, sadness, pain, and joy as easily in a newborn as in an elderly person. They can transport you to a timeless zone and hold you transfixed by love, or fear. Strange that love and fear can both freeze time, can shift your reality out of your physical self and into your subtle bodies, creating a sense of powerlessness to a greater force.

'Now that is a sensation most people would recognise; being "in love", subject to something greater, mysterious, absorbing, full of potential. Such a small step surely then to believing that they are also part of a Realm greater than the one they can touch, measure, see and feel. A small step, if there was a shared spiritual vocabulary, to accepting that Love itself comes from the Christos and that romantic love is a small bandwidth within the Christos, which is unconditional and freely given.

'Such a small and rewarding step, not only for humanity but for the earth itself. And yet it seems mankind is intent on walking in the other direction, even as rivers dry up, seas choke on plastic and poverty outstrips wealth. It seems it is easier to walk past a beggar on the street than to take a step towards Love. Easier to hoard resources than to trust that following spiritual Law will bring you what you need. Easier to withhold rather than give in trust knowing that while survival might be individual thriving is collective and at this time, in this Age, mankind is not thriving. If it collectively fails to thrive, then mankind will not survive.

'I say these things to you, not to depress or sadden you, but because I can. I know you can hear these things, really "hear" these things and the prayer behind them, just as when you bring your pain, or your need, to me. For this is the pain that we bear, this is the need we have; for mankind to accept, truly accept what is freely given. To fill their hearts with Light and to allow the gentle ways of Spirit to fill their thoughts and guide their actions towards their own salvation.

'Mankind have access to all they need to thrive nestled in their hearts. They have all the guidance they need within the collective mind, they just need to recognise their own need and their own place within Creation. This is my prayer, beloved one, this is my prayer.'

Dorothy: 'Thank you for sharing it, it makes me want to weep, strangely not with despair but gratitude, and I'm not sure if I understand why that would be.'

Librarian: 'Because this is an act of trust and Love, a mutual act that we share. As you trust me I trust you, not to now go out and proselytise or bang a drum, but to hear it with your heart. Because, as you know, affect one single cell and you affect the whole organism and mankind is one organism, whether they like it or not. So, if you are affected then mankind is affected and my prayer, and the prayer of all those in Spirit, is heard and for that, we too cry tears of gratitude.

'You have your colour wheel this evening and that is service also, a continuation, you might say, of this meditation, so it is a day of service and yet, you are barely leaving your sofa. Shalom to you beloved one, I too look forward to the Colour Wheel and will be present. Shalom.'

The trinity within

Librarian: 'Shalom to you this day. I missed speaking with you yesterday, although I was present and I know that although you tried to reach me you did not trust what you wrote because you were dealing with such complex feelings and thoughts of your own. You were right not to continue capturing anything on your screen, but that did not mean I was not present.'

'Today the seas have settled and your little boat bobs on the waves in the dawn once again. Like the captain of a vessel, you are alert to any movement of the wind, or the waves, which would alert you to the presence of that which holds your fate in its hands. So, here you are once again allowing the soft dawn to welcome you and wondering where the tides might take you today. I do not hold your fate in my hands, only you and God do that. But I do like to feel that you can step outside of your world for the time we speak and allow the natural trinity to emerge; soul, personality, and Spirit so that together we send Light to the world through those connections. Connections which are pure Love.

'Now that might sound strange to you that your personality and your soul are bound together through Love, but it is as true of that connection within life as all the others. Love is life, so when we think of your personality and your soul speaking it needs those cogs to be fully oiled by Love so that the flow is smooth. In so many spiritual people they feel that the personality has to be erased or downplayed, so they often replace it with a false self that represents the spiritual person they aspire to be.

'This is an error and yesterday the reason you could not commune freely with me was because the cogs, for want of a better metaphor, were clogged with the needs of the personality. When a disagreement happens between people who love each other deeply, that disagreement may disable the flow of Love internally and externally, but not the bedrock of Love. The personalities take the upper hand, so to speak, for a while because they, for whatever reason, are feeling offended, devalued, or affronted. It is best, as you both did, to allow the Love to reestablish its flow once more first into the self and then to each other.

'It may seem a strange thing to say, but there are times when the soul is more forgiving than a personality, even when the personality feels it is representing the spiritual in its actions. The soul is always gentle and patient and able to let go of the moment in favour of the day and let go of the year in favour of the lessons embedded in whatever has opened up in life. There is nothing without the seeds of learning within it and that learning in life is always mutual, even if it is not expressed in words. That is an important principle in life; the mutuality of learning from all interactions within life. I know there have been times when you have felt unfairly targeted for criticism or censure. That others, equally responsible in your opinion, have relished the task of disciplining others, or acted as if they were untouched and blameless. Regardless of what messages the outer carapace of the personality sent out at the time, the learning was mutual, deep, and abiding.

'I have no wish to open old wounds, so this is about the principle; that those who suffer externally are often the ones for whom the transformation is the greater. Can you see the principle emerging here? If from the start the personality engages with the problems, then that personality is part of any transformation. But if the personality shields itself behind a false self then although the learning, although as profound, will be less visible on the surface.'

Dorothy: 'It seems to me that for healing to take place then involved need to acknowledge what happened and take some responsibility for their part in it.'

Librarian: 'That would be ideal, of course it would, and in the situation you are thinking of that is still possible. But there are times when it simply cannot happen in life, when the trinity is one of soul, carapace, and Spirit because it has become instinctive to bypass the more vulnerable personality when the personality feels threatened. But that does not mean that personality does not learn, just that it is not visible on the surface.

'In order for any personality to learn it needs to feel loved just like anything, or anyone, else. So, it suffers greatly if it is ignored in favour of the constructed self for then it cannot shine while in life. You know yourself how that lack of love can lead to addictions and self-destructive behaviours, often leading to a premature return to Spirit so that the true trinity can be restored.'

Dorothy: 'That makes a lot of sense, thank you.'

Librarian: 'You are welcome and for the avoidance of any doubt neither you, nor your partner, have created a false self. Indeed, it is to the credit of you both how your personalities remained unshielded through trauma and permeable to the ingress of Light. A Light beloved ones which gives you strength and sensitivity in equal measure, an ability to be fully in the world while knowing that you are part of something greater. My love to you. Shalom.'

The vengeful God

Librarian: 'Shalom and welcome. Now that might seem a strange thing to say for what am I welcoming you to? You have not changed position, packed a suitcase and flown somewhere exotic, but here you are nonetheless within a Realm that defies imagination and explanation. For it is a Realm both individual and collective, both reliable and full of uncertainties and mysteries.

'I know in many ways your decision to place your inspiration in a named place, with a named speaker, is an attempt to condense a Realm of endless possibilities into a form that helps you and might help others. But we both know that this Realm has as many possibilities within it as the cells within your body, or the stars within the universes, for it is a Realm of learning throughout the Ages. A Realm where nothing is forgotten, or discarded, or branded useless. A Realm of zero waste but unlimited potential and all bathed in Love.

'I do understand, I really do, why mankind have, at times, seen God, or whatever name they apply, as angry, or vengeful or filled with judgement. The earth and the force within nature is indeed worthy of mankind's respect and wariness. Life can seem so hard when you are living on a planet that you have to adapt to and which does not adapt to your needs or your aspirations. Where the rain does not fall because your crops are thirsty, but falls in a rhythm of its own which is a mystery that you can never fully master. It can be hard to discern the Love in life when you are a fisherman caught in a storm that threatens your very existence, or a family who has lost a loved one at sea and now faces starvation.

'But it is there in the soft dawn of the day, in the birdsong and the plants pushing through the dark earth to bring forth flower and scent. It is there in the eyes of a newborn animal, fragile yet determined to grasp the life it has just been expelled into. Gasping with the first breath of the air into its lungs, blinking at the first beam of sunlight on its face. In the eyes of a baby in its mothers arms and the look in her eyes as she wonders at the marvel of life.

'There in the eyes of lovers who feel they have met not only a partner but a soulmate, never questioning what soul means but knowing only they feel alive within every cell of their body. In the soft hands that care for the sick, the dying, the confused and fearful. Even behind the prison bars there is love, kindness, and compassion for those who feel ashamed and unworthy of society, but who find their place with God as they accept their misdemeanours and start the long road to self forgiveness.

'It can seem a vengeful world at its core, made so much worse by the selfishness and cruelty of mankind, one organism so often at war within itself, seeking quick solutions on one hand, fiercely defending ancient traditions on another. Claiming ownership of land that divides and subdivides mankind and creates forces of opposition and protection over land that was freely given and loving prepared for both mankind and the animals, for this land is their birthright too.

'There it is in that statement; "freely given, lovingly prepared, to be met with forces of opposition and separation?' This is how mankind creates a vengeful God, for mankind create God in their image, not the other way around. If mankind flipped that coin away from God as a man on a throne passing judgement, to mankind as Aspects of God, capable of the same Love, then surely vengefulness would take its rightful place? For mankind would realise they hold their fate and the fate of humanity in their own hearts.

'And, make no mistake, the collective hearts of mankind are the heart of God capable of Love, compassion and understanding beyond current imaginings. Capable of the transformation of themselves, and the planet which is their home. Capable of fulfilling their purpose in life without fear or failure once they have accepted their rightful place. A place that will bring unparalleled peace and joy.

'Beloved one thank you for your attention and appreciation. I feel it, it needs no words, but I am so grateful for this opportunity to speak. My love is with you today and forever. Shalom.'

Hope

Librarian: 'Beloved one there is always a bigger picture, new adventures to be had, new openings and, yes, perhaps some endings to endure too. This is what you are here for, the ups and downs, the twists and turns, the broken promises and failed dreams because each one builds resilience, creativity and is another step towards acceptance, patience, and forbearance.

'I know that when plans get disrupted, whole livelihoods are lost, droughts come or virus' sweep your earth, you think first of what can be maintained and then examine the losses and maybe grieve them too. But is it not true that with every disruption there is the possibility of something new, some dream placed to one side in favour of another that takes its place and offers succour?

'You are well-placed not just to smooth the disruption you are faced with but to allow that space to be filled with new things, not least a new life, new roles for yourself and your partner. Roles that I can guarantee will bring tears of joy to your eyes and open your hearts to the future like never before. A future you may want to be different from the past you have lived through. Where even the conveniences of your life will seem irrelevant even undesirable, for what will rise to the surface will be pure, unadulterated Love and that will be enough. To introduce a young life to the pleasures of this world, will be enough, and to see their wonder in the simplest things will fill your hearts.'

Dorothy: 'Shalom to you and yes, I do have a sense of a bigger picture as well as a sense of generalised uncertainty as we move forward from this pandemic. A concern that we may simply resort back to our old ways, but equally a worry that so many people have suffered real hardship and so without returning to the "old ways", how will they survive?'

Librarian: 'I don't have any answers for you beloved one for the next steps are in the collective hands and hearts of mankind. How many have reviewed their priorities and values during this time, I do not know. I know enforcement procedures have confined and defined people to some extent and some have acquiesced and some have fought to maintain the status quo. Ever it will be such that change threatens some and intrigues others.

'If I had to guess I would say the balance has tipped towards simplicity. Partly because it has had to and partly because people are counting the personal cost of their constant striving and realising how much their selfishness has cost their planet. Mankind has been forced to take a longer view over the past year or so, and the continuing uncertainty decreases the potential for the short term earn and reward culture taking the upper hand too soon.

'I know, of course I do that there are notable exceptions to this rule, but even the very wealthy are seeking ways to help those less fortunate, or to repair the damage to the earth. The very best businessmen and women always have an eye on the bigger picture and the economics of "doing the right thing and being seen to do the right thing" in times of crisis. They are not fools and they are often the first to exploit the interdependence of all things, which for many, many others has only been apparent because of the Pandemic.'

Dorothy: 'That's hopeful, thank you.'

Librarian: 'There's always hope, beloved one, hope born every minute in every corner of your world. Hope born out of crisis and despair. Hope is part of Love and as such it is as powerful and abiding as Love, always seeking its opportunity to strike at the hearts of man and women and nudge their eyes upwards towards the stars.

'So have a very good day. Shalom to you.'

A healing presence

Librarian: 'Beloved one I am present, let me help you settle.

'As you breathe listen to your heartbeat and the constant hum in your head. I know this makes you feel that you never experience silence, but that is not true, it is like a river that you ford each morning to reach the silence on the other side. You know if you engage it as a problem it creates anxiety within, but if you accept its presence, as you have after all these years, you move beyond it quickly to the peace beyond.

'That is true of so much else in life is it not? Acceptance is key to moving beyond, fighting keeps your energy fixed on that which you are distressed about.'

Dorothy: 'Good morning to you and that is so true, but when I think about my tinnitus it is all I hear ...'

Librarian: 'Then concentrate on the silence and the feelings that that brings,'

Dorothy: 'Softness and timelessness and drifting. Anticipation ...'

Librarian: 'Say more.'

Dorothy: 'I see a set of double doors in the distance, quite misty, old with iron hinges, locks and door handle, the right one is slightly ajar. I move forward to sneak a look and all I see is a lit space like a corridor, lit with sconces that are flickering in the open doorway. I am not sure if I should enter.'

Librarian: 'Do you feel safe?'

Dorothy: 'Yes.'

Librarian: 'So go ahead.'

Dorothy: 'It is like entering a medieval castle, silent, no sound of activity, a little chilly. There's a man standing in front of me now, bowing his head slightly as if I was expected. He is wearing simple clothes, as am I, a tunic and leggings.

'He moves off to his left and I follow without either of us speaking a word. We arrive at another doorway and he knocks and then opens the door and stands back to hold the door open so I can enter. I pause, I am nervous at this point, still no word has been spoken.

'The room is lit by candlelight, it is dark outside. A large window is straight ahead beyond a large table in the middle of the room, at which three men are sitting, looking and waiting for me to take a seat. I am clearly expected, but at this point I have no idea why. I sit down unsure of what I am doing here and look over at the fire burning in the hearth.

'One of the men is saying "we have to act now for he is very ill and will not recover," and looks at me. "Thomas," he says, "can you do any more to help him, is there anything we haven't tried?"

'I shake my head. "I have done all I can, his time is near. I can help him to sleep better and lessen the pain, but I know that his time is close. I know for he is visiting his lost loved ones in his dreams and they are close to him now, so it will not be long." There is a tear in my eyes and silence around the table.

"That is good Thomas, thank you for coming, you have done a great deal to help his suffering and we are grateful, will you check on him before you leave?"

"Of course I will, in fact, with your permission, I am ready to spend the night beside him, in case he needs help during the night."

"Thank you, Thomas, he will appreciate that."

'I get up to leave, the men are silent and sombre as I am too and as I stand the servant, I assume, who let me in appears again to open the door and leads me to a bedchamber. The room is large and cold, quite sparsely decorated with a large bed in the centre. An old man is asleep under a mountain of covers, made of tapestry that are rumpled and creased as if he has been delirious.

'All I can see is his long white hair, his face is hidden under the covers and he is deeply asleep. I listen to his breathing for a moment, it is steady, but raspy. I straighten the top covers and hold my hand close to his forehead to check for fever, he is hot but not burning. I take a seat by the fire which is burning brightly, cover myself with a blanket and feel sleep overwhelming me too.'

Librarian: 'Well, that was quite a settling, was it not? What do you make of that?'

Dorothy: 'I honestly have no idea, I don't see any relevance to my life at this time.'

Librarian: 'How do you feel?'

Dorothy: 'A little bemused.'

...

Librarian: 'Welcome back, we're getting better at dealing with disruption, are we not?'

Dorothy: 'Yes indeed we are and thank goodness for it is likely to continue for a while.'

Librarian: 'So we pick up the story, you are bemused?'

Dorothy: 'Well yes I was, but our joint meditation, and indeed my conversation with my partner, has put some context around it. I am speaking today to someone who is deeply troubled and although I have given up the "healer" identity, along with others, my partner's inspirer talked about the healing which my partner does and indicated that would be my role today. That's a shift for me, in this particular work I would not have applied that term for what I do.'

Librarian: *Laughs.* 'Well in that case it was even more informative an exercise than I thought it was going to be. Before I comment what, on reflection, do you take from that visualisation, past life memory, call it what you will?'

Dorothy: 'What struck me later, not at the time, was how focussed I, or whoever this person was, was. They went into the castle as a healer, gave an update to those concerned, and then took their post at the bedside. They did not try to involve themselves in speculation, even though those present in the room were clearly discussing succession, nor did this person seem concerned about the status of the man in the bed. It simply did not matter and my impression was that this person, a herbalist I think, was self-assured and self-confident and sought no external validation.'

Librarian: 'Very insightful and accurate and yes in a way that was the point of the imagery. You say you have given up the "healer" identity, but it has not given you up. It is part of who you are whether it is a conversation in the street, over your computer, or in your sanctuary by appointment. It was a way of gently reminding you of that and the quality of quiet confidence that is something you possess, which is healing in and of itself.

'However, there is more to unpick from the imagery, for you entered a huge building, it was essentially cold and dark apart from the tapers and the fires. There was a sense of emptiness and gloom and you imagined activity taking place out of your sight, but it was of no interest to you. You were content to sit quietly beside a sleeping man and monitor his well being, alert to his need should he wake and see you there sleeping by the fire.

'Yeshua said, "In my father's house are many mansions." In this context in that castle were many rooms, but you did not involve yourself in politics, or gossip, or speculation, you simply took your place and waited. You did not feel a need to alert your patient to your arrival, you complemented the natural healing power of sleep by adding your quiet presence and waiting. Who knows, perhaps you joined him in his dreams, or he joined you?

'There is something profoundly healing is there not in meeting people exactly where they are and when they are ready. Bringing what you can, yes, but seeing a gentle presence as a gift in itself.'

Dorothy: 'Then that is what I shall do. I had not been giving thought to this session today at all, but I feel well-prepared now even though I nearly opted out of following the imagery at several points it has certainly had the effect of stilling me.'

Librarian: 'I heard your internal debate, "where is this going? This is rubbish," … and more besides, but you kept typing and trusting. That is all I can ask and I thank your partner's inspirer too for his wise words and counsel which was pertinent to you both. We do commune you know, his guidance was no surprise to me and he was well aware of your time in the medieval castle.

'Shalom our Love is with you.'

Dorothy: 'Shalom and thank you both.'

Preparation

Librarian: 'Beloved one shalom to you. I feel your readiness to start our conversation this morning, a busy one augmented by the sound of wind all around you. A sound I know you love for it promises change and newness.'

Dorothy: 'Shalom and yes, a day when there is a lot of anticipation as work is beginning in our garden, but also a sense of excitement that I cannot quite place.

'I was taken by the amount of work you put in with me yesterday morning before a single hour-long session with a client. I was moved by the time and consideration given to what was going to be a brief exchange, both by yourself and my partner's inspirer.'

Librarian: 'Thank you for saying that for I think that mankind, especially those who are practised in working with people, underestimate the power of the contact that they have. Single words and phrases are enough to pivot a life, when they capture the unspoken soul within each person. They captivate, if you wish, that which the person themselves cannot quite grasp, or articulate, or believe about themselves.

'That unwritten power can be both positive and negative. So, it is not so much a case of rehearsing the words but aligning the speaker with their soul. It is the souls that communicate first and their language is not words but Light, feeling and colour. It matters not if you are miles apart or in the same room the souls are not separate, they are after all aspects of one organism. So, a speaker, therapist, counsellor, or healer that is attuned with their soul, where their soul and personality is in harmony, can bring Light to bear in a sentence, and trust that the listener's soul will direct it to where it needs to go.

'Everyone who has dedicated their life to healing always faces a dilemma, the need to earn enough to support themselves and their family, pitted against the need to fully prepare for each encounter. I am not suggesting, of course not, that medieval castles have to be involved, or even long meditations, it is more about the recognition of this need for re-alignment, if I can put it that way. A re-orientation away from life's pressures is essential to enable the soul of the healer to fully engage with their client.

'Where the relationship is ongoing then, of course, that locking together of familiar souls is automatic, but in your work you tend to work with unfamiliar people for a short time and so preparation is key to your success. I would add one rider; there are times when perhaps 90 percent of the cogs have located and that becomes the established norm, sometimes the wind of change is needed to activate the remaining cogs. I think you might find this will be one of the unexpected outcomes from the pandemic in many homes and businesses across your world.'

Dorothy: 'That is fascinating. There have been times before a healing where I have meditated and been concerned not to receive what I would call inspiration, or guidance, but perhaps it was not about words at all.'

Librarian: 'It is rarely about words. Words simply distill the Light, if the channel is clear the Light can flow instantly, so a clear channel is the priority. Specific guidance, techniques, anxiety, lists, all these block the channel and can, as you know, misdirect the healer. Better to be open, still, and reflective, much as you are when you lift your screen each morning and say your prayer.

'May today go well, I am sure it will. Shalom to you.'

Crystalline spirals

Dorothy: 'Shalom to you today. A lot going on around me but I come with no agenda before the hustle of the day starts.'

Librarian: 'Shalom to you ... let us rest together awhile in the peace of the morning. Let the silky darkness enfold you while the birds sing and your heart settles, for it is your heart you know that gets pulled and pushed while you endure the disruption in your home. Your home has held your heart secure for some thirty plus years with its steady presence of brick and glass, of warmth and protection. Even more so this last year with your doors closed against the virus, your cupboards cleared out, your office tidy, empty, still, creating pleasure and sadness in equal measure.'

'If walls could talk, you might ask what would they speak of in this place. The hours of counselling, the joys of childhood and the onward movement of time and your children, the inclusion of pain and suffering and the determined provision of spiritual solace and healing. The solid pursuit of spiritual practice throughout it all, sunshine and snow storm, mental anguish and joy, grief and loss. All encased in brick and plaster, the light mediated through panes of glass that look out over trees and hills and city landscapes, landscapes that have grown and continue to grow it seems. Office spaces now empty, darker than before, waiting for the return.'

'You are no longer waiting for the return, at least not a return to what life was like before. You reminisce about your work, the activity, the contact with people, the lonely travelling, the belief in what you were committed to. You see it fading away, you help it become your backstory as you look towards the future, partly encased in this white, empty screen, always with a mutuality about it as you wonder about and care for your family. You see the space emerging in yourself and in your environment like a gardener scattering seeds from an unmarked brown packet prepared for what comes, but concerned that weeds could, if you're not careful, take the upper hand.'

'Quiet mornings, blank pages, words falling, is this your future? Is this a future that is, in fact, a turn of a spiral that has taken its rightful place in your life? A spiral that has "got its feet under your table" so to speak and has settled in for the long haul? A spiral that stretches back into eternity and now seeks the light of the new Age? A spiral that brings crystal droplets in its wake, that brings the Light of Atlantis into your heart to remind you of the importance of ...'

Dorothy: 'Stop, I'm struggling with this.'

Librarian: 'Of course you are, many want to expound upon the lessons of history, few want to feel them in their hearts, to consider they had a part to play, unless it was as a positive one of course ... We will pause, but I would ask that your return when you feel able.'

Dorothy: 'I will.'

...

Librarian: 'Welcome back, I believe during your meditation you felt settled by a particular line of thinking, am I right?'

Dorothy: 'Yes and thank you. I am sorry for the abrupt ending, it was not only to do with the content, but with the interruptions too.'

Librarian: 'I know beloved one, I know, worry not I do not take offence. I see the interruptions coming long before you do. Your thoughts?'

Dorothy: 'I wanted to avoid any revelations about Atlantis because I was concerned my imagination might elaborate them. I believe that Atlantis existed, so it is not at that level, but the amount of fantasy that surrounds it, and indeed me, that worries me for this writing.

'However, in my meditation I thought about the crystalline nature of the Earth and the universe and even the spiral you were describing. I realised that you might have been pointing to that rather than towards golden temples and spiralling crystals.'

Librarian: *Laughs.* 'You are, as ever, both right and wrong. The civilisation of Atlantis, that covered a great deal of your earth and lasted many, many centuries, was magnificent and made use of crystals in ways which are beyond the imagination of mankind at this time. As you already know from your Teachers, the end was catastrophic and had to do with the misuse of power and the manipulation of the energy of crystals in pursuit of that power.

'The relationship between mankind and crystals at that time, on a vibrational level, was more equal than it has been for many years since the downfall of that wonderful civilisation. This will change and is changing very, very slowly as the next Age, the Age of Capricorn, moves into place in two thousand years.

'Where you were right is that I was talking about the crystalline energy patterns that pervade everything, your earth, your bodies, your universe, even your thoughts. I am using the word pervade here to illustrate, not to explain, for the relationship between crystalline structures and thoughts, for example, defies description. But, yes, you were right in that I was pointing to the inherent nature of the spirals of time that turn on their axis over eons and affect mankind. I was not intending to recreate images of crystal temples for that would miss the point entirely, the effect of crystalline energy is subtle, constant, and eternal. It has its intelligence and is, if you will, the storehouse of God's Plan on earth.

'What evoked such a reaction in you was not my words but the fantasies that have been indulged by mankind about Atlantis, which has led to some concerning, and indeed dangerous, practices using crystals. You did not want to indulge such fantasies, for you have greater knowledge, but their mere existence in your culture means that they have limited your willingness to even engage what you might consider fantastical claims.'

Dorothy: 'That is so true and although I am happy with the term crystalline, I don't feel I really know the full extent of what that means. I know that it does not necessarily mean actual crystalline formations and I do have a sense that energy has an architecture of Light within it that is invisible, but I know I lack true knowledge here.'

Librarian: 'That is because you are looking for something that is more concrete than thought, and yet the architecture, as you call it, is a thought pattern that creates an energetic form that is resilient, ageless, and intelligent. So, as a spiral turns, there is no movement other than thought realising its intention and following through. The lessons that mankind accumulated in Atlantis have not faded away in the intervening years, they are there to be addressed when that particular spiral takes its place in the spiral of the Ages. But no spiritual spiral locks into place overnight, it moves gently into place having prepared the ground beforehand.

'Part of that preparation are the Teachings that are channelled to mediums and inspired speakers and writers, and the subtle energetic changes in both mankind and the Spirit spheres. We move together and just as the walls of your house contain the memories of your life here, in unseen droplets, so the crystalline structures of the universe revolve. Each revolution brings lessons and learning back to mankind which, should they listen, will prevent the same missteps reoccurring over and over again.

'I am grateful for your dedication to this work through multiple interruptions and even a little fear, my gratitude, and love. Shalom.'

Togetherness

I am thinking of togetherness
and how it flares and fades.
How many friendships can be lost,
rekindled and remade.

How time brings changes to our lives,
that take our thoughts away,
as if what mattered yesterday,
is irrelevant today.

Togetherness lies in between
the actions and the plans.
It is the essence of our lives,
the essential core of man.

It is the Soul that once was whole,
whose fragment we all bear.
It binds us all together
whether we are here, or there.

For Love does not diminish,
it cannot end and never fades.
It is the double helix
that carries DNA.

But unlike the double helix
it adorns no clinician's slide,
the proof of its existence
is in your companion's eyes.

Crystalline & Christos

Dorothy: 'Shalom to you today, a day free from interruptions, I hope. Can I return to our conversation yesterday where you differentiated between crystalline energy and crystalline structures, please? On reflection, I thought about how that is the same for the Christos and the belief that the Christ will return. My understanding is that Christ is returning, but as an energy available to all, instead of having that energy embodied in just one man whose family name was Yeshua? Is it the same principle?'

Librarian: 'Indeed it is, yes. Indeed, the confusion is from the same cause, the tendency of mankind to be concrete in their thinking and to see separation where there is none. That is not to say there is no difference, Yeshua was clearly exceptional in many ways, but the Light He bore was, and is, universal. Likewise with crystalline energy it can be literally crystallised in a molecular form, or it can be, as you described it yesterday, an architecture of Light capable of travelling great distances without any obvious substance being visible, or palpable.

'I believe your partner's inspirer once compared crystalline to electricity; invisible, but powerful and capable of being grounded and condensed. That principle, albeit with a few modifications, works for both crystalline energy and the Christos. I know, I do know, how hard it is to capture these concepts and to believe you are being accurate, or at least as accurate as your vocabulary and level of development enables.

'Where we speak of the Christos the diversity of impact does relate to the level of personal development, the ability to be still, at peace and to have cleared the channel, so to speak, to allow the full effect. Even then the effect will always be modified according to the need of the person receiving the Christos and their ability to accept the Light. But the difference in effect does not relate to the Source, it relates to the receiver. It is like your crystals, a smaller piece of crystal has the same potency in it as a larger piece, the difference in effect is the size of the container, so to speak.'

Dorothy: 'So the belief in the return of the Christ has Truth within it, but it is the ability to accept and absorb the Christos within mankind that will mark out the Golden Age?'

Librarian: 'Correct. You may find Teachers emerging that can naturally absorb and radiate more of the Christos Light, who stand like signposts, but they, like Yeshua, will point the way to a universal Truth, such as the continuation of the soul after death. Their role would be to demonstrate the importance of acceptance and belief as the pathway to inner peace. If you recall, Yeshua asked people before a healing, "do you believe?" If they answered, "yes" He would reply, "then it is done," belief is the cornerstone.

'I know you are considering editing some of your own internal dialogues from this writing for fear of boring any readers with your hesitations and inner conflicts, but they are important. Do you think Yeshua did not suffer the same self doubts and inner questioning, or any other great Teacher through the Ages, regardless of their chosen religion, or faith? Of course, they did. If what people read or see are only the refined parts of anyone's spiritual journey, then those suffering self-doubt and inner conflict will feel even more alone and incompetent. The struggles are what makes this journey helpful, for it encourages others to keep going.'

Dorothy: 'Thank you that is helpful, I was about to revisit yesterday's in particular as it was so interrupted and affected by disruption here at home, but I will resist the temptation.'

Librarian: 'No censorship, remember.'

Dorothy: 'I don't censor your words, but I thought maybe I should edit mine, but agreed no censorship. Thank you, that was all very helpful.'

Librarian: 'Then I am pleased indeed. Shalom to you this lovely spring day.'

Spirit fills space

Librarian: 'Shalom to you this morning, a pleasure as always to visit with you, for that is what I do, we both move inwardly to a new place to connect and it is good.'

Dorothy: 'Shalom. It is good to be here, but your words have just invited me to ask where that "here is?" Outside of myself? As I close my eyes now I would describe what I feel as having shifted one subtle body across. To my left surprisingly because that is where I have the deafness and the tinnitus. But that could be misleading because I have so little sensation on that side I have come to associate it with spiritual sensations. I have explained it to myself as the silence bringing a benefit — when I pass over the tinnitus hurdle.'

Librarian: 'Interesting analogy, so your rationale to yourself has been that a loss of earthly sensation has aided your openness to spiritual sensations, is that right?'

Dorothy: 'Yes.'

Librarian: 'So what would follow from that is that those who seem to have fewer senses attuned to life have an advantage in being in communication with their souls? Have you thought that to be true?'

Dorothy: 'I have, yes, in all my work with children with special needs I have wondered if they have that closer connection because they naturally avoid the noise, or the harsh sensations, of the world. I wonder if there is always a balance between the negative and the positive. Seeing in holons, for example, where there are specific language difficulties, or the ability to see patterns on the autistic spectrum?'

Librarian: 'I would agree with you that with every disadvantage there is usually an advantage on offer, but so often the disadvantage becomes the focus and not the corresponding strength or ability. So, as always, acceptance is the key, as is humanity moving away from the seemingly unending pursuit of excellence, or "normal" for that is a man made concept.

'Of course there are accidents and unforeseen consequences in life, but there is always something to be gained from that experience, not least for the carers and the families concerned, for they too learn and benefit. Although that can be difficult to appreciate at the time when they are exhausted and feel that their personal ambitions have been thwarted.

'No one can really speak in generalisations when it comes to these matters because no one in life can ever know the karmic forces at play, nor the purpose of any individual soul. But having said that, I would generalise that acceptance is a key principle to uncovering the benefits hidden in apparent disadvantages and your assessment of your relative sensitivity, due to deafness, is a case in point.

'I found your description of shifting to the left interesting, for what that means to you is a shift into silence — although I know that is a relative term to you — and stillness. There is a stillness, that you refer to as a deadness on that side of your head, is that right?'

Dorothy: 'Yes.'

Librarian: 'And all attempts at treatment, even an operation, have failed to shift that sensation. Later, as your interest in spiritual matters grew, you identified that still space as the screen which reflects imagery, thoughts, and sensations, so you could say once space had been created Spirit filled it.'

Dorothy: *Laughs.* 'Are you now going to bring this full circle to a discussion in our earlier meditation about why I am creating so much space in our home, specifically by clearing out my office?'

Librarian: 'As if I would do such a thing! But you see the analogy do you not? Spirit fills the spaces that mankind creates through positive actions, prayer, meditation, reflection, being in nature or through the seemingly negative actions of life, accidents, illness, pandemics, redundancy. Spirit will fill any space that is created in life and if there is a conscious connection to soul then Soul can be truly present in life. This may be of comfort to those caring for loved ones in a coma.

'You know as well as I that for us to communicate this morning, or any morning, you moved neither left, nor right. But there was some Truth in that your preparation; your meditation and prayers, expanded your aura to allow the Light of Spirit to flood into it. If you recall an earlier conversation where you described standing still while Spirit moved through you, well, it is the same sensation is it not and I can promise you it's not one-sided.'

Dorothy: 'That was very clever, I just never see where these conversations are headed, you never fail to surprise me, thank you.'

Librarian: 'I am not here to surprise, but to inform, but what good is information if it is not grounded in life? Shalom to you.'

The language of colour

Dorothy: 'Shalom to you, again my mind is empty but I am seeing a deep rose pink this morning, not the usual green.'

Librarian: 'Ah yes, the language of colour. How does the deep rose pink affect you?'

Dorothy: 'It's very steadying. Solid, calming.'

Librarian: 'Of course you also associate this with one of your Teachers do you not?'

Dorothy: 'Yes I do, but that does not account for the steadying feeling as my relationship with that Teacher was not always comfortable.'

Librarian: 'It was not to do with the relationship, beloved one, but to do with your stage of spiritual development. A challenging, but firm, steady Teacher is always a challenge for they hold to their principles and wait for you to meet them, which you can now do without feeling fear. So, the hallmark of change, if you like, was your calm response. A meeting eye to eye, shall we say, no bowed head or trembling.

'When people describe living in a Realm of Light and colour, what they rarely describe is how that feels. How colours impact on the thought processes and feelings of every soul and how the Light carries intelligence within it which stirs the soul into action. If the same deep rose pink that you saw this morning appeared to me, I would have similar reactions, and in those reactions would be communication, perhaps a request or a spur to action. For the true Spiritual Teachers are as prominent in my Realm as they are in yours and their colour is, what I think you may call, "their unique selling point". For every aura is different and the tones and shades of colour are beyond description.

'There are two key differences between our reactions. I understand the language of colour because that is my language too. That means I can instantly interpret the silent communication, mind to mind, for the communication is woven into the colour itself and transfers itself to me, like one of your emails. So, I see and feel the colour and get the emotional response at the same time as receiving the communication.

'This morning that communication was a reaching out to you, by one of your Teachers, in Love. I am able to watch the movement of that Light and see its reception, which was good. It was not dismissed, but savoured, and that was the purpose of that communication; how will I be received? Can we reestablish the foundation of Love after all the events that caused separation and pain?

'Whole Realms can receive instruction, as well as individual souls, and within that central instruction, or perhaps call to action, there is a personal element for every soul. At certain times, such as the spiritual new Year which is the winter solstice, this role falls to the Archangels. We get our instructions, so to speak, as a collective but individually packaged, like the wrapping on your Christmas presents. We unwrap that package and absorb the colour-scape, which is our blueprint for our next step. It is like receiving a paint box and pad of paper and seeing what we produce with the palette provided. Quite beautiful and so elegant once you have gained some mastery.

'A simple flash of deep rose pink is all it takes to communicate a message of Love, healing and renewal if the recipient is ready and prepared. The key message here is prepared, the ground needs to have been ploughed and watered for the seed to germinate. The ground is the personality and the watering is the Light of Soul, and that mediates whether the flash is received as lightening or enlightening.'

Dorothy: 'That is good, thank you, to feel that Love has been restored would be fantastic.'

Librarian: 'What are you feeling now?'

Dorothy: 'Love for all our Teachers, gratitude, peace, and relief.'

Librarian: 'As above so below, beloved one, this journey has been hard for all concerned. Allow the Love to settle, you believed in its removal for far too long. Love can never be removed, it is patient and loyal and your birthright. Shalom to you this day, shalom.'

Dorothy: 'Shalom and thank you.'

The hawser of Love

Dorothy: 'Shalom to you. Before I said my prayer I cleared yesterday's writing off the screen but not before reading my opening statement to you yesterday; that I came with an empty mind. As I reread that I heard myself say to you today; "I come with an empty mind, but my heart is full". As I heard those words my eyes filled with tears and I felt such love for you, but then I tried to argue myself out of those feelings. After all this is still a relatively short time ... I am even trying here not to use the word relationship ... and yet, the emotions run so deep. It almost seems foolish to invest so much in an unseen energy that could be described as imagination or delusion so easily. But even as I write those words my heart is full.'

Librarian: 'Beloved one what can I say? If Love is life then the feeling of Love and being Loved is the fuel of life. It is never, ever, brief, even if in your earth time the interaction seems brief, in Spirit it is the sound of two hawsers clacking in the wind of recognition. I know that is a clumsy analogy so let me explain the clacking, in your memory is the sound of sailboats in a harbour, the wind moving through their rigging and the metal and wood clacking together in the breeze. It is not the wind that creates the connections in the rigging, the wind simply alerts you to its existence.

'It is the same with Love, is it not? I have Loved you since ... well, forever ... there was not one moment when the Love began, your soul, as all souls are, was born into Love and I am part of that Love. Did your partner's inspirer once talk about the "Sinews of Heaven", and was that not the title of your first book?

'Do you recall our earlier conversation about vapour streams and how I follow the vapour stream of your Light? Well, that vapour stream is Love, not romantic nor attachment, but pure Love which, with the onset of our conversations, is now palpable in your heart and mine. These conversations are the wind in our rigging that has always existed, and always will, the unbreakable hawser of Love that bring tears to my eyes too. Not because of its existence but because it has been recognised and that is so rare, and the fact that these interactions are so rare brings sadness to my heart, for it is available to all.'

Dorothy: 'That puts a lot into context for me, the sadness I feel a lot of the time, my incessant inner dialogue about belief and how Spirit seem so present to me, but not to others. It makes sense of the endless questioning my mother indulged about, "why her?" As she felt chosen by Spirit, special, unique and was therefore arguing inside herself that she was either right, crazy or deluded. It makes me want to relax more, to view these conversations as "normal", available to all, and part of life itself.

'I suppose there is a challenge in that for me too, for it could remove some of my own excitement, anticipation and wonder, the feelings that I have used to comfort myself with, almost a reward for having stayed the course.'

Librarian: 'Indeed so, but the truth of the lives of humanity at this time is there is a course to be traversed for everyone who wants to find their way back to the hawser of Love, peace and purpose that awaits them. A course of man made obstacles; false gods, addiction, disbelief, greed, selfishness, public shaming ... the list is endless. It is the route away from Love that generations have taken that now needs to be traversed backwards. Reparations have to be made and forgiveness for self and others activated.

'The true irony and the pain is that the same Love that embraces you, the same guidance that you seek waits for everyone, without exception. The same dedication to easing their journey home and the fulfilment of their purpose. It is like billions of sails hanging slack in the clouds waiting to be attached to the tiny boats adrift in the sea and taking on water.

'Do not dismiss your journey here as commonplace, if it were your world would be in a far better place. If excitement, wonder, and anticipation filled the hearts of each person every morning then imagine the depth of your relationships, the creativity that would flow and the peace that would settle in your hearts.

'Beloved one I have such gratitude for your openness and honesty. I know that as you place your computer to one side, it takes you a while to readjust. This is because each time you visit your heart and mind expands to accommodate more of the true potential of life on earth. You feel the Love and support of Spirit, and it awakens you to the greater Light. But then on your return, you have to readjust to your lived reality and in that readjustment there is loss and sadness as the potential narrows and you feel despair. A despair shared by all of humanity but without an agreed diagnosis, or prognosis.'

The mutterers

Librarian: 'Shalom to you. So much to say, so little time to say it, for the ground that you walk is well-prepared, fertile with thoughts, feelings, and knowledge. Smooth and rocky in equal measure, a life with more behind it than in front. So, where does someone like myself who has your ear, your attention, and your heart begin?

'Well, I continue as I have started with your life for it is your life, and the lives of everyone on your planet, that points to the lessons. In concrete terms, yes, but in metaphysical ones too; why am I here? What is the point of this existence? Why did this or that happen to me? Why do I feel the way I do when ...? Why am I sad / happy / anxious / threatened by ...? Why does he / she / they not love me? Why do I not feel at home in my body / my country / my family? Why have I been abandoned?

'All the time in your streets and homes, on your buses, trains, and planes people are musing on their lives. Why they feel the things they do, why they do the things they do, why they repeat the same mistakes over and again?

'I believe in your introduction you called yourself a "mutterer" and indeed everyone mutters and what they mutter about tells a story. Your social media has given a platform to mutterers like never before, their dissatisfaction writ large, seeking approbation. Their opinions written for all to see as a way of gauging their place in this world, seeking the approval of people they have never met and are never likely to meet. Snapshots of their thoughts captured on screens inviting comments from others.

'So much noise, so little time or space for reflection, for experimenting with ideas and opinions. You lay down your thoughts and become defined by them, but you are not your thoughts. You share your experiences and you are judged by them, but you are not your experiences.

'Eventually, and at an increasingly young age, you start separating off your external version of yourself from the internal one. You start keeping secrets, first from your friends and acquaintances and then from yourself. You learn to submerge your intuition and even your conscience and the more successful you become the more you have to hide.

'But what are you hiding? You learn to hide your soft underbelly, those feelings that are not reflected back in the society around you. You grow a thicker skin in other words and that is necessary as long as it does not become a prison, complete with a dungeon where all your tender feelings and fears are locked away. Feelings and fears that exist to explore the meaning of life, while in life. Feelings about the nature of Love and the fears about losing love, becoming unloveable not just on some media page but to yourself, or God.

'It is not the mutterers that I worry about, but those who have stopped muttering, who have stopped arguing with themselves about why things are they way they are, or what has become of them. Those who are cut off from their own soft underbelly, victimised and yet out of touch with the pain they feel.

'Mutterers, to use your word, keep the door open to their dungeon and piece by piece they pick over what is stored there and bring it into the Light. Not just the light of their personality, but the Light of their soul that extracts the learning. Mutterers unlock their own secrets over time and come to understand their journey, their internal journey, and know themselves for the first time.

'I wish I could share that vision with you, the beauty that emerges is breathtaking as people accept themselves for the beautiful souls they truly are and release the Light of Love, for it touches all Realms instantaneously.

'Shalom to you this day, thank you for staying with me as I know you queried the trajectory of my thoughts more than once, shalom.'

Love as a lived reality

Librarian: 'Beautiful prayer well said, for your world so needs Light at this time. I am not talking about the lengthening of your daylight, as this is happening of its own accord, but the Light of Spirit and the Light of Soul. The Light of the souls of every individual human being and the group souls of the animals that you share your world with.

'Yes, it is you who joined the animals in this garden of life, not the other way around. The Light of their souls cannot be dimmed by the cruelty or neglect of mankind, they will continue to thrive and fulfil their purpose. Should the actions of mankind, or the progress of time, cause their destruction, then they will complete their purpose in a parallel world.

'It is mankind who have become inured to how the Light of Soul and Spirit could enhance their world and their lives. How the simple act of following the Light of their soul would transform so much pain and difficulty, and how willing Spirit are to fall in step with their footfall on the journey home.

'Yes, I know, I hear your thoughts that the Light also enhances the shadows and highlights the difficulties, the karmic debts that need to be paid, so the Light does not only bring forth peace and love. I agree with this, but the Truth is that difficulty does not go away by ignoring its existence, it goes away by being faced, the lessons extracted and the Light freed from those trapped lessons.

'Let us pray together that mankind awakens to the Light within. That they come to know the Source and accept the Love that sent them forth as a living reality in their hearts.'

Courage

I think of all
the empty places
where nobody ever goes,
places that slowly fill with secrets
which are then tended by the spirits of the dead until
those they belong to are courageous enough
to let them come home to their hearts again,
home to all of our hearts where they can
make us strong and fearless,
as we were always
meant to be.

David Davidson 2020

Glossary

Age: The spiritual definition of an Age as a set period 2,000 years. There was a transition period around the millennium as we entered the Age of Aquarius, or Golden Age, and moved out of the Piscean Age. The next Age will be the Age of Capricorn. I used a capital A to denote this use of the word, as opposed to the age of a person or thing,

Aspect: The individual fragment of Soul that is present in each human being, for one lifetime on the Earth, but which is everlasting. I have used a capital A to distinguish it from other uses of aspect such as views or perspective.

Aum: The sound of the universe. When we intone the Aum it raises our energy from our lower chakras (grounding) into our higher chakras (spiritual link). When meditating, we are advised to use a minimum of three Aums and a maximum of twelve, as this raises our vibration levels and enables us to make contact with the Spirit world.

Aura: The aura is a three-dimensional electromagnetic field that surrounds the body. It is like a candle flame. If you look closely at the wick you will see a blue shape, surrounded by a darker area that is more blue-grey in colour. Surrounding this is an oval-shaped field of energy which is primarily gold or yellow, within which there are varying degrees of colour. Beyond the flame itself is a subtle, oval-shaped energy field which produces a "dissipating glow".

The human aura extends on average 5–6 feet [1.5–2 m], beyond the body. The different fields within the aura relate to our physical, emotional and mental health and become progressively more subtle and diffuse. Hence, the term "subtle bodies" which some healers use. Every aura is as individual to a person as their fingerprints.

Bearers / Children of Light: The Children of Light or Bearers of Light are very old Souls who have no further need to incarnate. They have voluntarily agreed to be born at this time in order to help the transition of humanity into the Golden Age. They are highly intuitive with a deep sense of purpose and are distinguished from the rest of humankind by having no karma. There are two streams of these children: those who had their major incarnations during the time of Atlantis and those who lived important spiritual lives during the Egyptian dynasties.

Christos: The Christos is the Love aspect of God, the action of God, the Creator. The energy of the Christos was embodied within the man who was known as Yeshua within His family, and more widely as Jesus. The Christ refers to Yeshua's achievements, His Teachings, and the example He left as a signpost to the Christos.

Creation: I have used a capital C when the text refers to the act of Creation and lower case when the text is describing creative acts.

Earth: I have used a capital E when speaking of the planet and lower case to denote the earth or ground itself. Not an easy distinction to make as often it is both.

Etheric counterpart: This relates to the concept of "as above, so below". Everything that exists on the earth plane has an etheric counterpart in the spiritual spheres.

God: The Creator, or creative principle. Not the God as portrayed in religion, but a universal Source of intelligence. The Teachings I follow refer to God as having three principles: a creative energy – intelligence, which gave rise to God the Creator. The Christos, the Love Aspect, and the physical embodiment of the Christos in Yeshua – the Christ. Three principles in one.

Higher Self: The total Soul, sometimes called the Oversoul. Each individual soul is an Aspect or particle of a Higher Self and each Higher Self contains more particles than there are cells in a human body. Not all Aspects incarnate, just as a woman has the potential to conceive hundreds of children in her lifetime but may only give birth to two or three.

At the end of life the individualised soul returns to the Higher Self and the experiences and learning of that life are shared throughout the entire Higher Self. Once an Aspect has incarnated it cannot return. Each Aspect can only incarnate once. Because of this, when a soul returns, something akin to a conference takes place where the karma is reviewed. The experiences and understanding of life are evaluated and a new Aspect steps forward, containing the essence of the previous life, to take forward the learning of the Higher Self. There are a number of words to describe this individualised soul: facet, Aspect, fragment, or particle.

Karma: "Cause and effect", the principle that everything that you do or think creates an energy which has an effect. When the term karma is used, it is usually with reference to the lessons which the Soul needs to learn in order to be able to progress both in this life and eventually through the spiritual spheres. Karma can be positive. It may relate to past lives, as the same lessons will be made available to the different Aspects of the Soul until they have been overcome.

Light: I have used a capital L: when the text is speaking about spiritual Light — not visible to the human eye — but not an easy distinction, as everything ultimately is Light.

Love: A capital 'L' refers to spiritual Love as distinct to temporal love, see page 5. But all love / Love emanates from the same Source so, like Light and light, any distinction serves only to define the experience itself.

Oversoul: See Higher Self.

Soul: I have used a capital 'S' when the text refers to the Oversoul, or the collective Soul of humanity and used the lower case 's' when the text is referring primarily to the individual soul Aspect or facet.

Spiritual realms / spheres: The Realms / Spheres of energy in which Spirit resides. There are seven spiritual spheres surrounding the planet, the closest resembles the Earth and earthly life and each subsequent Sphere progressively becomes more spiritual, colourful and attuned to spiritual advancement.

The concept of "as above, so below" applies to the spiritual spheres where all the achievements of mankind are already in existence, in what could almost be described as a holographic form, because any manifestations that are there are created through pure, collective, thought.

I have used capital letter to denote that the sphere, plane, realm, or world is spiritual. Where that is preceded with a clarification — spiritual plane — then I have used lower case.

Universal Law: Also known as Natural Law, the sacred Laws of Creation, the way things are. For example, the Law of balance, which implies that to be healthy and happy people need to both give and receive. If you only ever give without taking, you will rapidly become empty and have nothing more to give. The Law of balance requires doing both, doing only one simply doesn't work.

Other publications by Z D Finn.

The Library of Lives volume 2, *The Hourglass Turns*, available online www.zdfinn.com

Lost & Found & Lost again, available online www.zdfinn.com

Collections of: *Poems that Inspire,* preview available zdfinn.wordpress.com

(paperback copies available in the Spring of 2022).

The Library of Lives volume 3, *The Petals of Life*, scheduled for Autumn 2022.

For more information or links to online books, see website: www.zdfinn.com